Cut Flower Grower's Handbook

Photographs by Arjen Huese and Lisa Juelich

Sweet pea illustrations by Kim Stephens

First edition published 2012.

Published in 2012 by

Lulu.com

Cut Flower Grower's Handbook

Cut Flower Grower's Handbook

Cut Flower Grower's Handbook

Dedicated to my beautiful wife Margaretha, without whom I never would have ventured into the world of flowers...

Cut Flower Grower's Handbook

Contents

Cut Flower Grower's Handbook

Introduction

Cut flower trade: an international affair

The production and sales of cut flowers has gone through dramatic changes in the last hundred years. At the beginning of the 20th century most cut flowers were grown by the local vegetable and flower grower, and sold either straight from his nursery or in his own shop in the town or village. A lot of flowers were also produced by the head gardeners responsible for the walled gardens of the numerous country estates across the country, chiefly for use in the main houses but sometimes produce was sold on to augment the head gardener's income. Many varieties of cut flowers were bred and propagated by the nurserymen and head gardeners themselves, and most of their production was sold and consumed within a 10 mile radius around their gardens.

Today the cut flower industry is an example of a completely globalised market, where flower varieties are being bred in high-tech greenhouses in Europe or the USA. Large scale production takes place in low-wage countries like Ecuador, Colombia or Kenya and the flowers are then flown back to Europe and the USA to be sold in supermarkets and flower shops in towns and cities. A vast dedicated trade and distribution network has been developed, with the Dutch auctions as the central hub. Delicate and perishable as flowers may be, they are being transported more than 4,000 miles from growers in developing countries, often on dedicated charter flights to Amsterdam from where they are being auctioned and transported on refrigerated lorries to flower shops in all other European countries.

Flower auction in Aalsmeer in the Netherlands. Trolleys with the actual flowers to be auctioned are being paraded beneath the auction 'clock'. Several hundred bidders watch two clocks simultaneously and within a few hours millions of flowers have found new owners.

More than £80 million worth of flowers are being sold and bought every day worldwide; today flowers are a big global business.

However, slowly the tide is turning and consumers and florists in the UK are starting to become aware of the environmental and human impact of this bizarre system. Across the country a new generation of small-scale flower growers is starting to emerge to take advantage of this increase in demand for locally grown, British cut flowers.

More than 90% of the flowers sold in the UK are imported from other countries, up from 80% in the year 2000. As late as in 1990, almost 50% of all flowers sold were still produced in the UK; commercial cut flower production in Britain has been in a fast and continuing decline.

Daffodil field in Cornwall

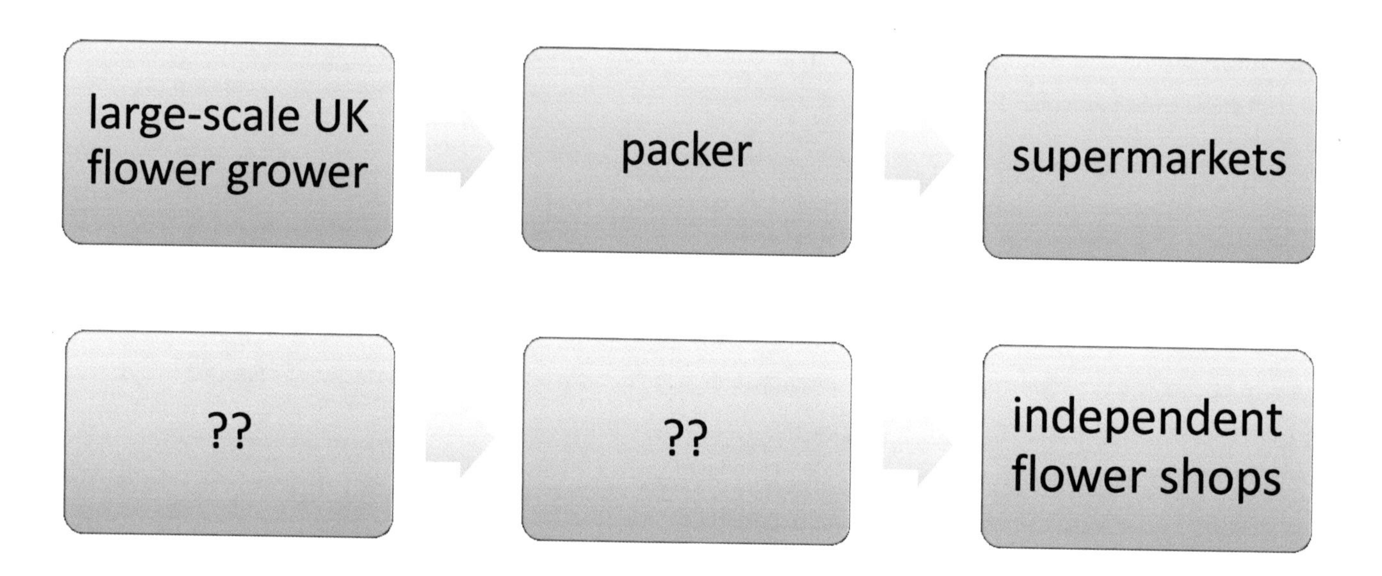

There are a few dozen large scale commercial cut flower growers left in the UK. Daffodils are grown on large fields in Cornwall and tulips and stocks in greenhouses around Spalding. These crops go straight to a few large packing houses where the flowers are being sleeved, labelled and prepared for distribution through the British supermarkets. The interesting fact is that the independent retailers, the shops who pride themselves on quality, freshness and a personal service, struggle to get hold of UK-grown flowers because they are not widely available from the wholesalers. So customers can walk into a Waitrose or Marks & Spencer's and see buckets full of flowers adorned with Union Jacks, but when they want a bespoke bouquet from their local flower shop they are rarely able to buy British. Many florists are painfully aware of the issue and welcome supplies from a local grower with open arms.

Here lies a huge opportunity for a new breed of flower grower. The production of cut flowers and foliage for a local market is a generous niche that is waiting to be filled.

Which market to supply

As a grower you can pitch your production and sales at three different levels: you can either grow flowers to sell directly to consumers, or you can sell to flower shops and wedding florists, or you can aim for the wholesalers.

Selling directly to consumers

Florists have a 200-300% mark-up on the flowers they sell to their customers, so a sunflower they buy in for 60p will leave the shop for around £1.50. That sounds like a very lucrative proposition, and any grower who can sell their sunflowers for £1.50 each is in a very enviable position indeed. The snatch is of course that most florists operate from expensive high street premises, have had several years of training in flower arranging and never sell every single flower they buy in – so their mark-up needs to allow for all those costs and losses. Perhaps at some point in the future every local grower will have their own shop in the village or town again, and can sell their flowers straight to the customer from their own premises. Until then, some growers have a stall on farmer's markets or fairs, and sell their flowers directly to the public. Other growers have their own wedding business, and provide ethical/organic wedding flowers to likeminded brides.

From a business perspective there are very few benefits from selling directly to customers, and a lot of downsides. Even though you might attract a higher price per stem for your flowers, that is by no means certain if you sell them on a farmer's market. You still have to account for unsold flowers, and you need to make sure you have the skills to create beautiful bouquets and hand-tieds. Selling to the public generally takes quite a lot of time, especially compared to the time it takes to sell to florists or wholesalers.

More importantly, you need to grow a really wide range of flowers, fillers and foliage for as many months per year as you can. You need a very intricate growing plan to make sure that you have at least ten or twenty different crops ready at any time of the market season, which probably runs from April to October, or even December if you try to cash in on the Christmas markets as well.

Potentially more lucrative is the wedding market. If you have flower arranging skills and can deal with the stress of handling demanding brides and their mothers, you might be able to make a good living from ethical weddings.

Another, lower-stress option is to offer mixed buckets of flowers for DIY-weddings. There is a great potential to cater for couples who are looking for a budget option for their wedding flowers, selling buckets with a mixed range of feature flowers, fillers and foliage for a fixed price. The brides or their mothers can then do their own arrangements. Brides can indicate their colour preferences, but the species and varieties are up to the grower. Mixed buckets with around a hundred stems are offered for between £35 and £50 per bucket.

Flower shops

This is the market with the greatest potential for most small-scale flower growers. Most florists are very keen on buying locally grown, English flowers – whereby English in this context not only means "grown in England" but tends to indicate traditional "cottage garden" type of flowers: Canterbury bells, peonies, campanula, scabiosa, veronica, garden roses, delphinium and larkspur, etc. These are all flowers that grow very well and easily in the UK so they are a good starting point for your conversations with the local florists.

The main benefit of selling directly to flower shops lies in the fact that they will buy several bunches of various flowers so as a grower you can sell larger quantities of the same crop. The actual selling process usually takes very little time: mostly it works via email, whereby you can send the florists a (twice) weekly update with available crops and prices, and they will email you back with their orders. You know how much to harvest and you know that every picked stem will be sold. Depending on the area you live in, you will be spending several hours per week delivering your flowers. In my case I do two delivery rounds per week and I spend four hours per round to deliver to around eight flowers shops, driving approximately a hundred miles per round. The best delivery days are Tuesdays and Fridays, which gives the florists fresh flowers at the beginning of the week and just before the weekend (when they sell most flowers). I have tried delivering on Mondays instead of Tuesdays, but most florists are not organised enough to submit their orders in time for harvesting (on Sundays!) and since I have moved to Tuesday deliveries everything runs much smoother.

You will still need quite a wide range of crops for most of the growing season, as each florist will only buy between 10 and 50 stems of any one crop (except sweet peas: 100-500 stems) so in order to have as large an order volume per shop as possible you still need between ten and twenty different crops at any one time.

Wholesalers

There are dozens of flower wholesalers across the country. If you do a search online you will be astonished how many you can find. Within an hour's drive around my garden there are at least ten different flower wholesalers, and unless you're in the Highlands you will probably find that that's the same in most places.

Every wholesaler I have been dealing with so far has expressed an interest in British flowers. Some of them will be willing to pick up flowers from your garden, and that is of course a huge benefit because of the savings in time and transport costs.

The prospect of dealing with a wholesaler can be quite daunting, but most of them will be able to deal with much smaller quantities than you think. They will buy quantities of hundreds of stems of most crops such as dahlias, sunflowers, zinnias and fillers like dill, ammi and bupleurum. Other crops may be traded in their thousands, but you shouldn't feel too small or insignificant to deal with your local wholesaler. The most important aspect is that you make sure that you come across as a professional who knows what they are doing. Make sure that your buckets are spotless, your flowers meet the standards and that you bunch your stems in tens and sleeve them. Use the Chrysal grower solutions in the water and make sure you agree on invoicing and payments.

If you don't know how the flowers look that the wholesalers are used to buying in, it is really helpful and fun to go and visit a wholesaler and look around the cold room and inspect their wares. You might be astonished to see how dirty the buckets are, or how awful and old some crops appear, but you can learn a lot about how the flowers are generally cut, bunched and sleeved in the trade.

Part 1: Cultivation

Part 1 of this book deals with the actual horticultural practice of cultivating cut flowers. We will go through the stages of planning, soil cultivation and fertilisation, transplant production, weed control, pests and diseases, support and protection, harvesting, post-harvest treatments and transport.

Most people get into flower production because of an inherent love of beauty, and of flowers in particular. But if we are going to make a living from flowers, we need to become a bit more pragmatic and start looking at them as a 'product' for sale. Don't worry – you can still enjoy the beauty and scent of these angels' kisses, but for now we need to get down to the practical facts.

What you need for a bouquet

Even for flower growers it is useful to know what you need for a bouquet – you may well decide that you're never going to make a bouquet in your entire life, but understanding the needs of the user (florist) is crucial when it comes to planning your garden and your crops.

Florists divide all floristry material in three different categories: focals (also known as feature flowers), fillers and foliage. The fourth F to make the perfect bouquet is "fragrance" – which can come from any of the three previous materials.

Focals are the main, big flowers in a bouquet. Often roses are used, but of course it can be any kind of big flower such as antirrhinum, zinnia, dahlia, calendula, hydrangea or celosia (the brain flower).

Fillers are the smaller flowers which are added to a bouquet to bulk it up and to add interesting shapes and "architecture". Baby's breath (gypsophila) is a classic filler in a bouquet of red roses but has been quite over-used and many florists are somewhat put off by it. Instead you can use achillea "The Pearl" if you need something white and small, and there is a whole range of umbelliferae such as ammi majus, ammi visnaga, dill, bronze fennel and the most recent addition is a first year flowering purple carrot called daucus carota "Black Knight". All of these add an ethereal spaciousness to a bouquet. Other great fillers are eryngium planum (the small-flowered ones are good fillers, the big ones are more a focal type of flower), salvium horminum (clary sage) and euphorbia rotundifolia. A different type of filler are stems with berries; you can think of hypericum in red, pink, green and ivory, or symphoricarpos (snowberry) and callicarpa bodinieri (beautyberry). For autumnal arrangements you can even go as far as to use thornless blackberries (with green fruit) or Japanese wineberry.

Foliage consists of any type of greenery which is added for the natural look, and usually consists only of leaves: bupleurum griffithii is very popular, as is eucalyptus gunnii. Other useful types of foliage are pittosporum tenuifolium, senecio greyii, physocarpus opulifolius "Diablo" and asparagus. Bells of Ireland (molucella) can be categorised among the foliages as well, although you actually use the green flower calyxes. I have also been experimenting with an ornamental basil ("Cardinal" from Genesis Seeds in

Israel) which, when grown in the greenhouse, yielded tall stems with shiny scented leaves. You can also grow this as a filler if you wait for the flowers.

Planning

Planning which crops to grow, and which not

Many new and enthusiastic flower growers set out to grow all sorts of flowers they like, and which you can find in the gardening seed catalogues. When I started I did just that, I had a look through the common seed catalogues and chose the flowers that had a scissor symbol next to them, and which I recognised from gardens or from the wild. Big mistake: I chose the wrong species, the wrong colours and I didn't know the most important attributes of a good cut flower...

Florists are interested in flowers with the following characteristics:

1. Species: it is very helpful if the species you grow are familiar to the florists. Of course you can grow some novelties as an experiment, but don't float your whole business on what *you* think is going to be the next top cut flower species because it probably won't. It is a good idea to grow some of the mainstays, such as sunflowers, antirrhinums and peonies for example, and grow some small quantities of new introductions.
   On the other hand there is no point in trying to compete with the main run-of-the-mill flowers which are being grown on an industrial scale in Holland, Kenya and South America: standard roses, chrysanthemums, carnations, lilies and tulips are all grown by specialist businesses in huge quantities and are cheap commodities in our current society. There is very little point trying to make money with tulips if you pay 15p per bulb and the florists can buy tulips from Holland for 10p or less!
2. Stem length: anything with a stem length less than 50 cm will be very difficult to sell – with one exception: sweet peas. Florists need long stems for their arrangements, hand-tieds and bouquets.
3. Colour: colours are a fashion-type of thing – certain colours are very popular at the moment, and other colours are extremely unpopular. Yellow for example is currently very unfashionable, the only exception is sunflower, which has to be yellow and not any of the modern fancy browns or greens. Fashionable colours are green flowers, burgundy, blue and for weddings white and pink are always in demand. Orange seems to be a colour which is getting increasingly popular.
4. Vase life: flowers need to last at least a week in the vase. Certain flowers, such as sweet peas and dahlias, struggle to make it through a whole week, but harvested and sold fresh from the garden (and sweet peas treated with silver thiosulphate) even these flowers will pass the vase life test. This is an area where local flower growers have a huge advantage over the overseas producers whose flowers will always be at least 2-3 days old by the time they arrive in the shops in Britain.

5. Scent: certain flowers are renowned for their scent: sweet peas, sweet William, stocks, etc. The stocks from Italy may look sturdy and beautiful but they have no scent at all – here the local growers can distinguish themselves from the international bulk by growing varieties that are extra scented.
6. British grown, locally grown: there is an increasing demand for British grown flowers, to support the British grower and the British economy. By using the Union Jack on your sleeves you show your customers where their flowers have been grown.
7. Organically grown: to be really honest in the UK there is a very limited demand specifically for organically grown flowers, unlike in the Netherlands and Germany. However there are some ethical wedding florists who cater specifically for this segment of the market. It is an extra selling point, but it won't be easy to attract a higher price for your flowers. I have always been an organic / biodynamic grower and wouldn't dream of using nasty chemicals on my land, but in the case of flowers there is no financial incentive to grow organically at this stage.

Species

The following chart shows the best-selling flowers in the UK in 2006:

1. Rose
2. Carnation
3. Lily
4. Chrysanthemum
5. Narcissus/Daffodil
6. Tulip
7. Freesia
8. Sunflower
9. Alstroemeria
10. Gladiolus

The most popular cut flowers in the UK, when consumers are asked:

1. Rose
2. Lily of the Valley
3. Freesia
4. Sweet Pea
5. Alstroemeria
6. Gerbera
7. Tulip
8. Narcissus/Daffodil
9. Dendrobium orchid
10. Hyacinth

All the best-selling flowers are produced in huge quantities by large scale growers in various parts of the world. Therefore, most of these flowers must be considered global commodities and it is rarely a worthwhile exercise to try to compete with the global market and grow these species in your gardens. The only exception is sunflower – even though it is being sold in large quantities, it is still a relative expensive flower for florists to buy and therefore worthwhile to grow. This is probably due to the fact that sunflowers are so bulky and heavy which adds considerably to the transport costs – in the space of one bucket with 50 sunflowers a Dutch lorry can carry 200 or more carnations...

The chart with the most favourite flowers is very interesting because here we find on position 4 the sweet peas which are hugely popular but not being produced on any scale in the Netherlands. The other advantage (for us) of sweet peas is the fact that they have a relatively short vase life and don't travel well and therefore are not being grown in any tropical low-wage countries. Here is a big opportunity for local growers!

Planning your production

Different growing habits of crops

For planning purposes we distinguish 8 different growing habits of crops:

1. Shrubs
2. Perennials
3. First-Year-Flowering Perennials
4. Biennials
5. Once-sown hardy annuals
6. Once-sown tender annuals
7. Batch-sown hardy annuals
8. Batch-sown tender annuals
9. Bulbs

1. Shrubs

When we think of cut flowers, our thoughts don't usually immediately turn to shrubs for cutting. However, in a changing climate in which summers get wetter and less predictable, and where slugs and snails can completely obliterate freshly sown or planted crops of annuals, shrubs can be a life-saver and a secure source of feature flowers (hydrangeas, viburnum, lilacs, roses), fillers (spirea, symphoricarpos, hypericum) and foliage (cotinus, physocarpus, senecio).

Shrubs are propagated once and then stay in the ground for several years. All shrubs we use in cut flower production are hardy, so can be propagated even at a time of the year when there are frosts. Some shrubs will flower in the first year after propagating, but usually the stems are too short to be useful and it is better to leave them on the plants so that they can establish themselves properly and be strong and healthy for production in the second year. Many shrubs can be propagated quite easily from cuttings, such as hypericum, senecio greyii, hydrangea, viburnum and spirea. Usually we will propagate them from mid-summer to late autumn, and in the greenhouse with bottom heat most shrubs for cutting will root quite easily.

Each of the shrubs has its own natural flowering season and often there is not much we can do to change that. There is a very complex and elaborate way of forcing lilacs which is being practiced by a handful of specialised Dutch lilac growers, but it is not something which I would recommend.

Harvesting times can be prolonged through the use of different varieties: there are early berrying hypericums, mid-season types and late varieties – by using several different varieties you can extend your harvesting season. Each hypericum will only have useable berries for about three weeks, but by choosing the right sequence of cultivars the harvesting period can be spread over 2-3 months.

2. Perennials

Perennials can be established from seeds or through divisions or cuttings. Seed-grown perennials usually don't flower in the year they've been sown, except the "first year flowering" perennials (FYF – you will find this abbreviation in most seed catalogues and it can be a reason to choose a certain variety when you need the flowers in the first year). Some of these perennials can be sown in autumn, and when they receive winter cold (vernalisation) they will then flower after the winter. I have successfully done this with eryngium and delphinium.

Perennials from divisions or cuttings are for example peonies and dahlias. Peonies don't like to be transplanted and need two to three years of undisturbed growth before you start harvesting stems.

Planning perennials is similar to the shrubs – usually there is not much we can do to have an earlier or later crop than the natural flowering season. However, by using different early, mid-season and late-flowering types you can sometimes create a more continuous harvesting window.

Examples of seed-grown perennials are campanula, physostegia, eryngium, echinops, stachys, etc.

3. First-Year-Flowering Perennials

First year flowering perennials will flower in the first year after sowing, although often later than in subsequent years. They are grateful subjects as you will get a return for your efforts in the same year as you went through all the effort of establishing them. They can even be grown as annuals, but often production increases and stems get longer in the second year. Examples are achillea, artichoke, lupins, etc.

Sometimes seed companies offer perennial seed which is especially primed and will flower in the first year. And seed companies also breed perennials which are usually second year flowering to be first year flowering – often at a premium price.

In terms of planning your FYF perennials there is often not too much you can do about having an earlier or later harvest – we are usually bound to the natural flowering season of these crops.

4. Biennials

There are not a lot of biennials in production as cut flowers, but they can be very useful because they usually give a crop very early in the season when there isn't much else yet. One of the most important biennials is sweet William, which you sow the year before it flowers. It grows all the bulk of its roots and leaves in the first year, and will shoot straight into flower early spring in the second year. Another biennial that we grow is Canterbury bells.

There are also first-year-flowering sweet William varieties on the market ("Hollandia" and "Bodestolz"), which will flower later in the season than the overwintered crop. So if you are keen to have a longer harvesting season of sweet William, you could grow a biennial variety as well as an annual type, and have them flower more or less after each other, although there will probably be a gap between them. I have found the annual types to be rather short and the seed too expensive – the overwintering type works very well for me.

5 and 6. Once-sown annuals (hardy and tender)

Many annuals only have to be sown once, and will then continue to produce large quantities of flowers throughout the season. Think of zinnias: for every flower that you pick the plant grows two new ones! Cosmos and annual scabious are other examples where we usually just do one sowing and keep picking throughout the season.

With these crops the trick is to try to get the plants to start flowering as early as possible and to keep them going. Zinnias have a high heat requirement and are frost-tender, so there is no point to try to be very early with these. They germinate very rapidly in a hot greenhouse, and your transplants will be ready within three weeks. Best sow them late (end of April) and plant them out when the soil and the air are warm outside.

Scabious is frost hardy and can be started sooner than the zinnias, and can be planted out early May.

7 and 8. Batch-sown annuals (hardy and tender)

These are the crops where we can and have to do most planning work: each batch of these crops will just be harvested once, or for a limited period, and then be rotavated in again. Here we need to work with batches: you sow these crops every week, or every two or three weeks, and subsequently plant them out every two-three weeks, in order to have a continuous supply of these flowers for as long as you can.

Sunflowers are a good example of a batch-sown tender annual: as soon as any risk of frost is over we transplant new seedlings every (other) week. The variety we use ("Procut Orange F1") takes about 3 months from sowing to harvesting, although it may even go faster in the heat of the summer.

Other examples of batch-sown hardy annuals are: ammi, dill, clary sage, antirrhinum, bupleurum and stocks. Batch-sown tender annuals are amaranthus and sunflowers.

I also treat my sweet peas as batch-sown annuals: I have a batch in the greenhouse over winter (winter sweet peas), and then two or three batches outside. In my gardens, a sweet pea crop gets picked for four to five weeks, and then I move on to the next crop. After four weeks the stems get shorter, the crop too high, and the general quality declines. I find it better to just start picking from the next crop rather than pruning, sideshooting and lowering sweet peas (cordon culture) in order to prolong the season.

9. Bulbs

Bulbs deserve a paragraph on their own, even though they are often grown either as annuals or as perennials. Some bulbs are tender and need to be lifted at the end of the growing season, and other types can stay in the ground and will slowly increase in size and even multiply themselves. Many bulb crops are being grown in vast quantities by large-scale growers, often involving different companies for multiplying the bulbs and forcing the flowers. Tulips are rarely worthwhile as they are grown on such a large scale, and the same applies to daffodils. However there are some bulb-type crops that might be profitable, especially alliums but I have also heard good reports of ornithogalum arabicum (chincherinchee) and tritileia "Queen Fabiola".

Recommended crops

Feature flowers

The feature flowers are the main big bold flowers in a bouquet. Think of roses, peonies and zinnias. Sunflowers are a bit an odd one as they are rarely used in bouquets, but would certainly be classified as feature flowers. Sweet peas are an odd one too as they are not often used in mixed bouquets, but they are so characteristic and even charismatic that they classify as a feature flower.

Allium "Purple Sensation" is the standard variety.

Top feature flowers

The following feature flowers are the tried and trusted mainstays at Wealden Flowers and I would recommend growing them in most situations:

Allium

Alliums have to be planted in autumn and will give a good crop of useful flowers in spring. Usually the bulbs are lifted and dried in June or July after the leaves have turned yellow and the bulbs have gone dormant. This gives the grower the opportunity to deal with the weeds as alliums are not very competitive. Instead of lifting, some growers cover the beds with mulch fabric to smother the weeds and leave it on until the alliums start sprouting in spring. Then they take off the cover and the alliums grow in a clean and weed free bed!

Recommended varieties: Allium aflatunense "Purple Sensation" is the most common cut flower allium. The bulbs are very cheap to buy and it is a reliable cropper. All florists know it and love it and the price is generally very acceptable. There are many other varieties to experiment with, but the high price of the bulbs makes it unlikely to be very profitable, and the market for huge allium flowers is very limited even though they look stunningly impressive...

Antirrhinum "Rocket" is a good variety for outdoor production.

Antirrhinum

Antirrhinum is an annual crop which can be grown in succession all year round (including heated greenhouses). In an unheated greenhouse you can plant them in December/January and have your first crop in May. Antirrhinums are popular and versatile, and even

A bed of Karma Choc, a very popular dahlia

Dahlia Karma Fiesta

Dahlia Karma Thalia

outdoors you can have a continuous supply for many months of the year through the use of successional planting.

Recommended varieties: there are many different varieties of antirrhinum, but make sure you use varieties specifically bred for cut flower production and not the much shorter bedding types. We have successfully used: Overture (for greenhouse production) and Rocket (outdoor production).

Dahlia

Dahlias are very popular even though they have a bad reputation for short vase life. Because your flowers will be two to three days fresher than the imports, your dahlias will last long enough, and you can build up a reputation for good quality dahlias.

Most dahlias will freeze to death or drown during the winter in the UK, so lifting and storing is recommended. A good place to store dahlias is in an earth cellar, or even a deep hole in the ground, in net sacks used for onions. The underground storage keeps the tubers moist but not wet, which they need to prevent them from drying out.

In early spring you can pot up your tubers in the greenhouse and take stem cuttings which root very easily, before you plant out the mother tubers. Even the new cuttings will go on to produce flowers in the same year. Be aware though that many dahlias are PBR-protected and propagation without a licence is illegal.

Recommended varieties: In Holland a lot of breeding has gone into dahlias to make them more suitable for cut flower production and the Karma series is the result of this. Karma Naomi is the earliest and most productive of this family, highly recommended. Karma Maarten Zwaan is a very useful white dahlia and Karma Thalia and Karma Fiesta are two great vibrant colours. Karma Choc is a popular deep maroon, but not the most productive of them all. In the USA Café au Lait is a very popular dahlia among cut flower growers and increasingly so in the UK.

Delphinium

Delphiniums are an amazingly popular cut flower. The only problem is that slugs love it so much – you can only grow delphiniums if you are blessed with an area without too many slugs. Organic as well as conventional growers often use mulch fabric (Mypex™) to prevent weeds from outcompeting delphiniums.

Delphiniums need to be treated with silver thiosulphate (Chrysal AVB) after harvesting to prevent petal drop, but the high price and high demand make them a worthwhile crop.

Recommended varieties: Volkerfrieden is a vegetatively propagated variety which is very popular and sold in large quantities through the Dutch auctions and into the UK. Other modern hybrids such as the Millenium series are very beautiful too. In recent trials "Centurion White" and "Magic Fountain Cherry Blossom" were found to be extremely strong and survived growing conditions much better than varieties in the "Aurora", "Guardian" and "Candles" series.

Hydrangea

Hydrangeas are high-value flowers in blue, white and pink. There are two different types of hydrangeas: varieties that flower on last year's wood, and varieties that flower on this year's freshly grown wood. Hydrangea stems are not always fully frost-hardy, so if your plants die back in winter and you grow a variety of the first type, you will have a year without flowers. It is much better to grow hydrangeas which flower on this year's wood, so called remontant varieties. You can prune these varieties back to 10 to 15 cm from the ground in spring and the plants will send up new long, strong, straight shoots with flowers at the ends.

The colour of most hydrangea varieties is dependent on the acidity of the soil and the availability of aluminium ions. To change the colour of your hydrangeas to pink you need to prevent the uptake of aluminium. This can be done by adding dolomitic lime several times a year to raise the pH to between 6.0 and 6.4. To obtain blue flowers the pH needs to be between 5.2 and 5.5 and aluminium ions need to be available, which can be added in the form of an aluminium sulphate solution.

Hydrangea Annabelle in full production

A bucket of hydrangea "Annabelle" ready for the shops.

Larkspur grown in support netting

Harvesting peonies

Sarah Bernhardt is one of the most popular peony varieties, unfortunately it is quite susceptible to botrytis, a fungal disease. Keeping the crop dry in spring by using Spanish tunnels is an option, or a regular spray with an (organic) fungicide like potassium bicarbonate (baking powder).

Hydrangeas have a tendency to go droopy after harvesting; the best way to prevent this is to dip the stems in a jar of aluminium sulphate powder (alum) straight after cutting and before you put them in a bucket with water. Alum has a mild disinfecting effect and helps to keep the stems healthy and turgid. It is important that the florist and customer use flower food with hydrangeas, it extends the vase life from just five days to at least fifteen days!

Recommended varieties: We grow a large patch of hydrangea "Annabelle", which is white and very attractive. They do need horizontal support netting though, as the flowers are very big and the stems would otherwise fall over in a strong wind. Hydrangea "Bodensee" is a good coloured variety.

Larkspur

Sometimes known as the annual delphinium, larkspur is very popular as well, although the price per stem is much lower. Larkspurs make up for that by growing large quantities of useable sideshoots, so the turnover per square metre might be at least as much as for delphinium. If slugs are not a big issue you can sow larkspur directly in the field, otherwise you can grow transplants first in early spring and plant them out as soon as you can handle them. Larkspur can grow very tall and the use of support netting is recommended.

Larkspur needs to be treated with silver thiosulphate after harvest.

Recommended varieties: all double varieties are good, they tend to shatter their petals less than the single varieties. We have successfully used "Tall Hyacinth Flowered Mix" and "QIS mix".

Peonies

Peonies are perennials with very showy flowers which appear usually during a three week period starting late May. There are not many different varieties to choose from, and interestingly most varieties have been bred decades ago. This means that they are not PBR-protected and can be freely propagated, usually through root divisions. After planting the roots, the plants need to be kept undisturbed for at least three years before you can start harvesting flowers. When you harvest the flowers you need to make sure that you leave at least one or two leaves at the plant from each stem as peonies only send out flowering shoot and no stems with only leaves. Picking all flower shoots with all the leaves would inhibit further photosynthesis and the peony plants would suffer badly.

If you grow organically it is advisable to grow your peonies through polypropylene mulch fabric and ideally under Spanish tunnels to keep them dry during the flowering season to keep botrytis off.

Recommended varieties: "Sarah Bernhardt" (big and pink, but susceptible to botrytis), "Duchesse de Nemours" (big and white), "Kansas" (hot pink), "Red Charm" (big and red).

Phlox

Phlox is a popular flower, and even though the prices aren't too high there is a good demand for these flowers. Some good varieties have been developed specifically for cut flower production, with tall stems and good disease resistance. Phloxes are perennials, and are very vigorous growers. In the first year after planting, about four stems can be harvested per plant; from the second year onwards production increases to ten stems per plant.

Recommended varieties: "Laura" and "Eden's Crush" (modern varieties with strong disease resistance), "Miss Pepper", "Miss Holland", "Snowcap", "Rembrandt", "Eva Cullum", "Blue Paradise" and "Blue Boy".

Sunflower

Sunflowers are a valuable crop; they can contribute significantly to your overall turnover and I recommend them to every grower. There is a lot of demand for them, but only for the traditional deep yellow varieties with a dark heart. Modern versions with brown petals or green centres seem attractive but don't sell. If slug pressure isn't too high you can sow sunflowers directly in the field and cover the beds with fleece against birds (crows love sunflower seeds). If that is too onerous you can try dying the seeds blue with food dye, apparently that confuses the birds. It is possible to pinch sunflowers when they are about 20-30cm high, which will result in 3 to 5 smaller sunflowers for which you will probably get a lower price each but a higher price in total. Check first with your florists to see whether they are interested in mini-sunflowers – often they

A healthy sunflower crop a few days before the optimum picking stage

A Procut Orange F1 flower ready to pick

Smaller sized sunflowers can be very useful for mixed bouquets, such as here with statice and calendula.

A collection of winter sweet peas: "Oyama's Bicolour", "Solstice Maroon", "Princess" and "Polar Star". The marker is 14 cm long.

"Natural" production of winter sweet peas: "Oyama's Bicolour" and "Black Prince".

like them because they can be incorporated in mixed bouquets much more easily.

If slug pressure is too high, you will have to grow transplants first and plant them out in the field once they have two pairs of true leaves. Sunflowers don't mind being transplanted but the flowers are already somewhat smaller than a directly-drilled crop so I wouldn't necessarily pinch a transplanted crop.

Recommended varieties: there are many different sunflower varieties on the market – what you need is pollen-less hybrids: they don't shed pollen on customers' tablecloths which is something undesirable. "Procut Orange F1" is my favourite variety, but "Zoar F1" (organic seed available) and "Sunrich Orange F1" are fine as well. "Procut" are the fastest growing series.

Sweet peas

If you have a protected area (greenhouse, polytunnel, Spanish tunnel), sweet peas are probably the most rewarding crop to grow. Production is limited to Holland and the UK, as these flowers are too fragile to be transported from South America, Israel or Kenya. The British public love sweet peas and there are too few quality stems on the market every year.

Sweet peas can be grown as cordons, which involves taking off every sideshoot and winding individual stems around their own strings hanging from the overhead wires. If your overhead wires are 2.20 metres from the ground, you can use about 5 metre of string wound on a special metal reel which hooks on the wire. When the sweet pea stems reach the wire, you can unwind a metre of string from the reel and "layer" the sweet pea stems on the ground. The result of this is that after a while every plant will have a few metres of stem lying on the ground, before trailing up towards the wire. This way you can make a sweet pea cordon last much longer, as you don't have to quit production when the plants become too tall.

Cordon production is quite labour intensive and most Dutch growers grow sweet peas "naturally" which means that they let them climb up vertical support netting. This technique is much easier but does result in some bendy stems, but total production is much higher and there is less work involved. Each crop of sweet peas grown in the "natural" way can produce for about 4-6 weeks, so successional planting is recommended to extend the growing season.

Winter sweet peas are sown in September or October before being potted up in 7cm pots in November in a frost-free propagation house. In January, when the days start to lengthen again, the plants are planted out in a greenhouse or polytunnel, and usually production starts at the end of March or beginning of April without additional heating – a heated crop will start sooner.

Summer sweet peas can be sown in batches from December or January onwards, usually a batch every 4-6 weeks. When the winter sweet peas are finished, the first crop of summer sweet peas is then ready to take over when grown in an unheated greenhouse. If the summer sweet peas are grown outdoors there is often a two-week gap between the last winter sweet peas and the first summer stems, which is not good for your marketing.

Sweet pea petals get damaged by rain, the coloured varieties more so than the white, but in any case for a top quality product it is highly recommended to grow them under cover.

After harvesting it is essential to treat the stems overnight with a silver thiosulphate solution to prevent petal drop and ensure that your sweet peas don't damage the fragile reputation of this wonderful crop.

Recommended varieties: Winter: "Oyama's Violet" (violet), "Oyama's Bicolour" (mauve/lavender), "Soltice Rose" (hot pink). Summer: "Mrs Bernard Jones" (pink), "White Frills" (white), "Our Harry" (blue), "Eclipse" (violet).

Viburnum opulus roseum

Viburnums are mainly grown for their green balls of flowers in spring. They are extremely popular with the florists, even though they are hard to hydrate and prevent from flopping. They are not the easiest crop to propagate but if you have a mist unit with bottom heat they will grow a vigorous root system within 4 weeks from cuttings taken in July or August.

Recommended varieties: there is only the species Viburnum opulus roseum, also known as Viburnum opulus sterilis.

Mixture of "Our Harry", "Eclipse" and "Jilly"

In Japan sweet pea bunches with some sweet pea foliage are very popular.

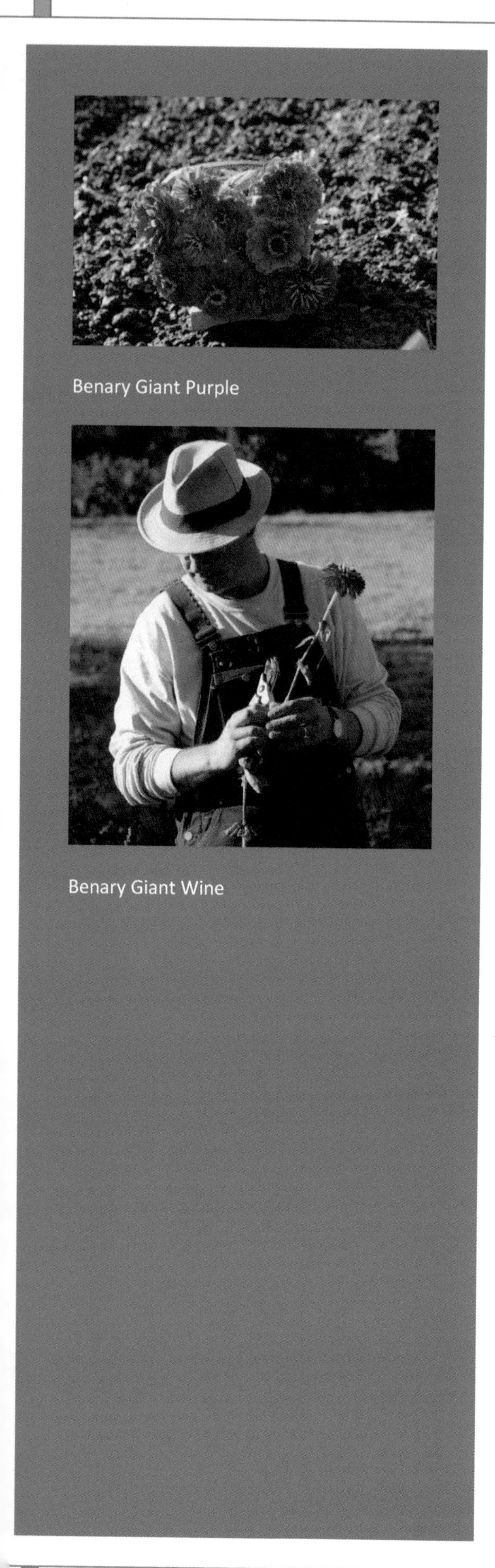

Benary Giant Purple

Benary Giant Wine

Zinnia

Zinnias are a great outdoor alternative to gerberas which can only be grown in greenhouses. Zinnias come in a wide range of colours, from yellows and pinks to deep burgundy and even lime green. Zinnias have a hollow section of stem just below the flowers which makes them slightly vulnerable to rough handling, and it is always recommended to sleeve them after harvest.

Recommended varieties: insist on "Benary's Giants": not only are the flowers big and the stems tall, but most importantly the stems are really fat which gives them strength and a long vase life. There are many other varieties none of which I would recommend for cut flower production.

Worth trying feature flowers

The following feature flowers are worth trying:

Aconitum

Aconitum is the lesser-known sister of the delphinium, and only half as popular. Quite undeservedly because aconitum has the same striking blue flower spikes, and is a lot easier to grow as slugs don't like it. Aconitum can best be bought as established plants from a (trade) nursery, and can be easily propagated further through dividing the clumps in early spring.

Recommended varieties: all varieties are useful.

Agapanthus

With their huge heads of blue flowers, agapanthus are a great focal in landscape plantings. They are also used as a cut flower, although I am doubtful about the quantities that can be sold through flower shops due to their large size and difficulty to incorporate in bouquets and hand-tieds. But I'm sure there is a market for a limited amount, for pedestals and large wedding work.

Agapanthus is not terribly frost hardy, minimum is -4 C. Commercial growers in Holland cover their crops in winter with a combination of straw and fleece. They plant 20-40 buds per square metre (each plant has one to ten buds) and full production of around 30 stems per square metre doesn't start until the third year.

Recommended varieties: Blue: "Columba", "Dr Brouwer", "Intermedia", "Wolga", "Donau", "Sunfield". White: "Corinne", "Polar Ice".

Echinacea and rudbeckia

Until recently echinacea only came in one colour: pink; but in the last five years a large number of new varieties have hit the market. Echinaceas with illustrious names such as "Tomato Soup", "Tangerine Dream" and "Hot Lava" are now available in a range of eye-popping colours and have the potential to transform the market for echinacea. Echinaceas are perennials, and the closely related rudbeckias are often annuals. Most rudbeckias are yellow flowered and therefore not too popular in flower shops, but T&M have a red variety called "Cherry Brandy".

A special type of perennial rudbeckia is "Green Wizard" which has flowers without petals and is a nice architectural addition to flower arrangements. The same effect can be obtained by peeling off the petals of normal echinaceas.

Another perennial rudbeckia is "Henry Eilers", with spoon-shaped yellow petals. This has been the number one perennial cut flower in several annual surveys among the members of the American Association of Specialty Cut Flower Growers (ASCFG).

Recommended varieties: choose echinaceas with petals which do not droop but stay horizontal; rudbeckia "Green Wizard" and "Henry Eilers".

Gladiolus

Gladioli are a widely traded item in the flower markets. They are relatively easy to grow and the corms are cheap to buy. However, each gladiolus stem has a very short harvesting window, the time when it is ready to pick but not too far open yet. Gladioli need to be picked when the lowest flowers on the spike are just showing colour; if the flowers are already open it is too late and often these flowers get damaged in transit. Therefore it is important to plant gladioli corms successionally: every week or every fortnight between early April and early June you need to plant another batch in order to have a continuous supply of gladiolus stems.

Pink echinacea

Rudbeckia "Henry Eilers"

Gnarled old lilac bushes on a Dutch nursery. These plants are dug up and forced in the greenhouse for lilac flower production. Once the flowers have been harvested, the bushes go back to the waiting beds outside to recover for several years before the next round of forcing. In this way the Dutch can supply top quality lilac flowers year-round.

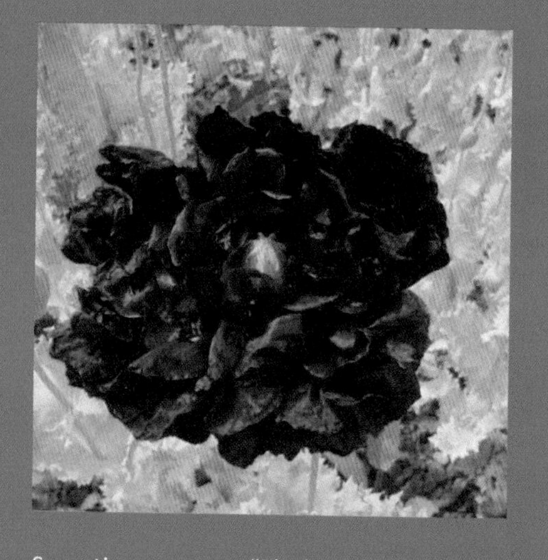

Sumptious papaver "Black Peony"

Lilac

Lilac takes a long time to grow to productive stage from cuttings or from micropropagated plants. After mid-June all vegetative growth stops in lilacs, so it is important to fertilise them well in spring, in order to make sure that enough stem length is achieved in the first few months of the growing season.

Lilacs (Syringa vulgaris) have a short harvesting season of about two weeks. Syringa hyacinthiflora flowers seven to ten days before the main species and the species Syringa prestoniae flowers about two weeks after S. vulgaris, so by choosing a range of varieties from these three species a longer harvesting season can be achieved.

Recommended varieties: "Sensation", "Krasavitsa Moskovy", "Monique Lemoine" (not "Mme Lemoine"!), "Agincourt Beauty", "Zanamaya Lenina", "Edith Cavell", "Avalanche", "Ludwig von Spat", "Etna", "Ellen Wilmott".

Poppy (Papaver)

Many people think that poppies don't last as a cut flower, but the double flowered oriental poppies are actually quite good. They develop big blousy blooms, reminiscent of peonies – and at a time when there are no peonies around. The poppy stems will bleed a milky sap and spoil the water for themselves and other flowers, therefore the stem ends need to be seared with a torch or briefly dipped in boiling water.

Poppies can also be grown for their seedpods, and that is what most florists will be familiar with. Find varieties with large seedpods, or try the "Hens & Chickens" which has several rings of tiny seedpods around the main seedhead.

Recommended varieties: "Black Peony", "Hens & Chickens"

Roses

Originally roses were regarded as the queen of all flowers, the most special of all blooms. These days roses are a plain commodity product, produced on an enormous scale in countries like Kenya, Colombia and Ecuador. Working conditions in these massive flower farms often leave a lot to be desired, and the impact on the environment of the unbridled water and pesticide use can be quite devastating, not to mention the carbon emissions of flying these flowers 5,000 miles across the globe to be in the UK in time for Valentine's day. Most of these roses are of the standard hybrid tea variety, and quite often the buds don't even open in the vase. All scent has been bred out of these varieties in order to achieve a maximum storage (transport) life. Because of the low cost of labour, and the low cost of transport, florists in the UK can often buy these roses for as little as 20 or 30p – the queen of all flowers has become cheap and nasty.

Obviously British growers can't compete with these cheap import roses, and there are only very few rose growers left in this country. However, there are customers and florists who will pay good money for traditional "Victorian" roses. The British breeder David Austin has trademarked the term "English Rose" and the term is now used for the round, "cabbage type" roses, often with quartered petals and usually scented. There is a good demand for this type of rose, many brides insist on these vintage looking, romantic and traditional roses.

Apart from David Austin there are several German breeders who are increasingly bringing excellent "Victorian" rose varieties on the market, often with excellent vase life.

Roses are best grown in Spanish tunnels, in beds covered with mulch fabric (Mypex™). The roses can be grown in double rows, 50 cm apart and 50 cm between the plants in the row. During the winter the polythene cover gets stripped off the structure to allow the roses to experience the winter cold, which improves flower production in summer. In spring the hoops are being re-covered with polythene and the roses irrigated with driptape or individual drippers.

All in all, my best rose for outdoor production has been "Sweet Antique" which has consistently produced tall stems, good strong healthy foliage and small pink spray "Victorian"-type flowers,

Arjen with a nice bunch of rosa "Sweet Antique" (Kordes).

A view over the trial fields of Rosen Tantau in Germany.

The traditional "cup-shaped" flower type is especially popular for weddings. These varieties can be sold as "Victorian", "traditional" or "garden" roses. Here rosa "Chippendale" (Tantau).

Stock production at Wealden Flowers...

... and large scale stock production in Spalding.

which I usually pick with one or two flowers open surrounded by several buds - giving it a really rich and gardeny look. I would only plant spray roses, ideally with the "Victorian" shape. The main big blousy feature roses give you only one perfect moment to pick, and if you miss that moment, the whole stem is wasted. If you don't pick every day, and sell every day, a spray rose is a much safer bet, as you can always nip out a flower or two that have keeled over and there will still be more buds and flowers coming. There is a real need for more spray roses with a tall stem, healthy foliage, good flower shape, sturdy petals (rain proof), very slowly opening, and a scent...

Recommended varieties: We have successfully grown the following varieties outdoors without cover: "Sweet Antique" (pink spray type, scented, Kordes), "Piano" (bigger red spray type, not scented, Tantau), "Pink Piano" (bigger pink spray type, not scented, Tantau)

Stocks

Stocks are easy to grow in the winter in a cold greenhouse or polytunnel for harvest in April or May. Outdoor crops are often plagued by flea beetles which are very difficult to control and outdoor stock production is not recommended.

Stock varieties can be single or double flowered. There is no market for single stocks, but unfortunately there is no 100% double flowering stock available as it is genetically impossible to create. Most stock varieties are "selectable double" which means that when the seedlings are subjected to cold temperatures, the genetically double flowered plants turn greyish, whereas the singles look much more vigorous and healthy. This is the moment when the grower needs to select: throw the healthy ones away and nurse the sickly looking seedlings on – they will give a double flowered crop! There are also Japanese and American varieties which are not selectable but give between 70 and 90% double flowering plants – which is acceptable.

Recommended varieties: "Katz" series, "Japan All Double White Surf" (90% double), "Japan High Double Series" (70% double), "Goldcut" series (selectable in seedling stage)

Special interest feature flowers

The following range of feature flowers are really only worth growing if you have a specialty market (perhaps certain wedding florists specifically asking for them):

Artichoke and cardoon

Artichokes and cardoons produce large thistle-type of flowers in a beautiful shade of blue. The market for these flowers is limited but the price is good, so it might be useful to grow a small area of these crops. In order to have a range of sizes, it is a good idea to give half of them the Chelsea chop: when the flower stems appear, cut them off at 20-30 cm height for several smaller flower heads.

If there turns out not to be a market for them, they will make a great addition to a Mediterranean style dinner! These crops are very susceptible to water logging and won't survive hard frosts so give them a sheltered spot in a well-drained location.

Recommended varieties: any variety will do.

Calendula

There are some really good varieties of calendula (pot marigold) for cutting, but the problem is always vase life. With or without pre-treatment, with or without flower food: it is difficult to get more than five days of vase life out of a calendula. As long as your customers are happy with that it is a great flower for mixed bouquets for example with small sunflowers and purple statice.

Recommended varieties: "Princess Orange with a Black Heart"

Campanula

Campanulas are very popular with florists for the English country look, and will always sell. They usually come in blue, white and pink shades, and all are popular. Most of these are short-lived perennials which are not very competitive against weeds, so growing them in landscape fabric is recommended.

Recommended varieties: "Campana" series, "Champion" series, "Muse" series (all of these hybrids are first year flowering, which makes life much easier even though the seed is much more expensive).

Canterbury bells

Calendula "Princess Orange with a Black Heart"

Canterbury bells

Celosia production is restricted to the greenhouse.

A bunch of celosia ready for the shops. In the background some clary sage.

Canterbury bells are a typical English cottage garden flower which is not grown very much commercially. Some florists absolutely adore it, but being a biennial it is more laborious to grow than annuals and there is a risk of outwintering or rabbits using it as winter forage. It definitely needs protection from rabbits.

Recommended varieties: there is only one variety: Campanula medium calycanthema "Cup & Saucer Mix"

Celosia

There are three types of celosia: the plumose (plumy type), the spicata (spiky type) and the cristata (cockscomb type). Celosia is somewhat related to amaranthus but unfortunately needs even more warmth, so can only be successfully grown in a greenhouse or polytunnel. Especially the cockscomb type attracts quite a high price per stem so might be worthwhile, although they are quite demanding in fertility and regular irrigation (use a timer).

Recommended varieties: "Supercrest", "Cramer's Burgundy"

Clematis

You see clematis increasingly in flower shops, and there is certainly a market for it, as long as the stems are tall enough. You could also grow clematis for its decorative seed heads. Clematis is a climber, so you will need a trellis or a wall to grow it against.

Recommended varieties: The flower arranger's favourite is Clematis "Durandii" which has strong stems and the best vase life of all. Others include "Duchess of Edinburgh", "Mme le Coultre", "Vyvyan Pennell", "Walter Pennell", "Polish Spirit", "Niobe", "Elizabeth". For seed heads: Clematis macropetala "Bluebird".

Digitalis

The normal wild digitalis is very common around Sussex so there is very little demand for it as a cut flower – people regard it as a weed. But a lot of breeding has gone lately into new colours and varieties with flowers all around the stem, especially by Thompson & Morgan, and some of these varieties may be suitable for cut flower production.

Recommended varieties: check the most recent T&M catalogue for the latest in digitalis breeding.

Hollyhock

Hollyhocks are another pretty cottage garden type of flower. Its vase life isn't too bad, but its main drawback is the fact that the leaves are almost always covered in brown pustules known as "rust" – so unless you strip down all the leaves it looks rather unsightly. Limited potential.

Recommended varieties: try the double flowered varieties which have a better vase life than the singles. "Fiesta Time" is relatively short which may be an advantage.

Lupin

Lupins come in a huge range of colours, and have a good vase life. The main disadvantage is that lupins have a very short harvesting window – less than two weeks. For a crop which is relatively unknown as a cut flower among the florists, that is too short a period to introduce them and expect them to be included in the regular orders and bought in sufficient quantities. As soon as the florists will have got used to them, their harvest season is finished already...

White digitalis

Hollyhock "Fiesta Time"

Tall variety of alchemilla mollis: "Thriller"

Clary sage "Blue Monday"

Fillers

Fillers are the small flowers or other materials (seed capsules, berries) that are added to the bouquet, often with a complementary colour compared to the feature flowers, or sometimes a contracting colour. Examples are baby's breath (gypsophila), statice and hypericum.

Top fillers

Alchemilla mollis

Lady's mantle is a very popular filler, which is not grown by too many Dutch growers, so there are opportunities here. The plants can be established easily from seeds; it is important however to grow the recommended varieties as the stems of the species are generally too short. Even the recommended varieties won't give useable stems in their first year, but from the second year onwards you can expect numerous stems of at least 40 cm. The stems are not very strong so they certainly need support, usually provided in the form of horizontal netting. Alchemilla can easily be overgrown by weeds so growing it in landscape fabric is recommended.

Recommended varieties: "Thriller" and "Robustica"

Amaranthus

There are many different types of amaranthus, but the one with the long drooping tassels (love-lies-bleeding) is the most popular one. Some florists prefer green, others red; so a mixture is called for. In normal years amaranthus will grow and crop well when grown outside, during extremely bad summers it will suffer and the stems will remain short.

Recommended varieties: Amaranthus caudatus red, Amaranthus caudatus green

Clary sage

Clary is a great filler which is easy to grow, and quite popular. When harvesting this crop we don't actually count the stems but make generous bunches of equal diameter, which saves us time and offers great value to the florists.

Recommended varieties: "Clary Blue Monday", Clary series mixture

Dill, ammi, fennel, daucus, orlaya

There is quite a large group of filler flowers from the umbelliferae plant family, which includes dill, ammi majus, ammi visnaga, fennel, daucus carota and orlaya. All of these except fennel are grown as annuals – as germination is slow they are usually grown as transplants before being planted out in the field. Most need horizontal support netting to keep the stems straight and upright in exposed locations. Ammi majus, dill and daucus carota are popular with rabbits, ammi visnaga and fennel surprisingly are not...

All of these are popular fillers, and demand is good.

Recommended varieties:
dill: "Mariska"
ammi majus, ammi visnaga, orlaya: (no varieties available, just the species)
daucus carota: "Black Knight"
fennel: "Bronze Fennel"

Three fabulous fillers: green dill (real dill), red dill (daucus carota "Black Knight") and white dill (ammi visnaga)

Eryngium

Eryngium is a perennial thistle with electric blue stems and flower cones. It is relatively popular and attracts a good price. There are two different types: the large flowered varieties and the small headed species. The large flowered ones are a good feature flower and the small headed types are mainly used as a filler. Eryngium can be grown from seeds, and when sown in autumn will produce the next year. Wait until the stems turn quite woody otherwise they will flop over. The stems are first green before they turn blue, the mature green stems are popular as well as the blue ones.

Eryngium gets really tall – at least 80 cm.

Euphorbia oblongata

Hypericum "Magical Red Fall"

Molucella

Recommended varieties: "Miss Wilmot's Ghost" (large flowered), eryngium planum (small flowered)

Euphorbia

There are many different species of euphorbia, and quite a few may be suitable as cut flowers. Euphorbia oblongata and euphorbia rotundifolia are two species which we have successfully been growing. Both are perennials and even though you will get some stems in the first year, they might be relatively short. From the second year onwards you can expect strong tall stems suitable for florists. All euphorbias ooze a milky sap from the stems when cut; it is best to let the stems bleed in a bucket of their own for several hours before selling them or mixing them with other flowers. The sap will spoil the water for other flowers, and block the xylem resulting in reduced vase life.

Recommended varieties: Euphorbia oblongata, euphorbia rotundifolia.

Hypericum

Hypericum is grown for its coloured berries which appear after the yellow flowers are gone. There are varieties with red, pink, green or ivory coloured berries, most of which are PBR-protected. However you can quite easily develop your own variety from seeds, just make sure that your new seedlings are rust-resistant: rust is a major disease in hypericum and will turn the leaves completely brown. Once you have developed a good strain you can easily propagate hypericum through cuttings.

Recommended varieties: all the "Magical" varieties from Kolster in Holland are specifically bred for cut flower production, and are rust resistant and tall.

Molucella

Bells of Ireland are a great filler, and most florists are familiar with them. Unfortunately slugs and caterpillars like them too, so you need to protect them somewhat. They are difficult to germinate: the trick is to keep the seeds for four to six weeks in the fridge before you sow them. It is not so easy to achieve a long enough stem on molucella; they need a rich soil and plenty of moisture. There are no varieties, just the species.

Nigella

No country wedding is complete without nigella, also known as love-in-a-mist. This is a versatile crop which you can sell at both flower and seed stage. There are beautiful blue varieties which are almost indistinguishable from cornflower blue, as well as snow white ones. The developing seedpod creates an amazing contrast in the white varieties. There are varieties with various colours and shapes of seedpod, all very popular. Nigella is best sown in several batches throughout the spring and early summer, to have a continuous supply of both flowers and seedpods.

Recommended varieties: "Albion" series, "Transformer", "African Bride" (pure white), "Curiosity" (deep blue) and "Midnight" (velvety blue).

Nigella "Midnight Blue"

Panicum (and other grasses)

There is a market for ornamental grasses, but it is not so easy to find good species and varieties which are suitable as a cut flower or filler. Panicum elegans is useful, as is Pennisetum villosum. Both need to be grown in a rich soil in a sunny location to make sure the stems are long enough.

Recommended varieties: Panicum elegans "Frosted Explosion", Pennisetum villosum "Cream Falls"

Nigella "Double White"

Scabiosa

There are annual and perennial types of scabiosa, and both are good cut flowers. The most beautiful ones are the perennials, but the range of colours is limited to shades of blue and white. Among the annual scabiosa you will find reds and deep maroons as well as the blues and whites. The perennials have bigger outer petals, which makes them really stand out, but the annuals are much easier to grow and the seeds are much cheaper too.

Recommended varieties: Annual: "Blue Cockade", "Black Knight", "CutBrite Formula Mix". Perennial: "Fama F1" is the top variety, but the seeds are horrendously expensive. Other good varieties include "Compliment", "Isaac House's Hybrids" and the "Perfecta" series.

Scabiosa "Black Knight"

Healthy crop of statice "Supreme Blue Erect"

Sweet William ready for despatch...

Statice

Statice is a wonderful crop without major pests or diseases, not even the slugs like it very much. You have to sow it early in spring and make sure the transplants get subjected to cold temperatures which induces flower production. Most florists have only seen blue and white statice, but there many other colours such as pink, yellow, and various pastel colours. Having said that, blue and white are the most popular...

Recommended varieties: "Supreme Erect Blue", other colours of the "Supreme" series.

Sweet William

Sweet William is one of the few crops that is still grown on a large scale in the UK by growers around the Wash (Boston area). Sweet William can be grown as an annual using specific varieties, but the seeds of those varieties are very expensive compared to the biennial types. The other problem is that often the annual types struggle to achieve sufficient stem length – therefore the biennial varieties are recommended. You can sow sweet William in spring and let it develop strong and big rosettes, which overwinter easily in most parts of the UK. The next spring you will be able to harvest a crop at a time when there isn't much else, giving some welcome cashflow. Sweet William is a cheap flower because it is produced so abundantly in the UK, but a quality crop can still be sold at a premium.

Recommended varieties: "Electron F1"

Worth trying fillers

Achillea

Achillea, or yarrow, is a useful filler. It grows easily in most places, and is a short-lived perennial. Achillea comes is several colours but the most popular colour seems to be deep red. After a while the stems tend to get shorter so it is a good idea to renew a third or a quarter of your patch every year. Achillea ptarmica is a slightly different type of flower, it has small white flowers somewhat reminiscent of Baby's Breath (gypsophila), and is probably more popular than yarrow. Make sure you choose a double flowered variety of Achillea ptarmica.

Recommended varieties: Achillea millefolium: "Cassis", "Cerise Queen", "Flowerburst" series, "Summer Berries". Achillea ptarmica: "Benary's Pearl" (reselected).

Agastache

Agastache comes originally from Mexico and is in the mint family. It forms straight sturdy stems of 50-60 cm with scented leaves and a flower spike. We always pick the stems before the actual flowers appear since they tend to get brown and drop off quite quickly. Picked at the slightly earlier stage, agastache is a very useful addition to your filler assortment.

Recommended varieties: Agastache foeniculum "Blue Spike" and "Snow Spike".

Astilbe

Astilbe forms white, pink and red plumes which are quite in demand by florists. They are not easy to grow from seeds, so buying plants from a (trade) nursery is recommended. Once you have established plants you can increase your stock by dividing the plants. There are many different varieties to choose from.

Astrantia

Very popular filler flower, in various shades between white and red. Astrantia is not easy to grow from seeds so it's best to buy plants from a (trade) nursery and propagate them further yourself through division in spring.

Recommended varieties: "Ruby Wedding", "Hadspen Blood", "Alba".

Cerinthe

Pretty blue hanging bells which can be harvested quite early in the season. This exotic looking plant is actually frost hardy, so can be planted out in March or April for an early crop. Not a common florist crop but many florists like it.

Cornflowers

Florists won't usually buy cornflowers as a shop item, but they are very popular for country weddings because of their amazing colour and their romantic feel. Don't grow the white, red or

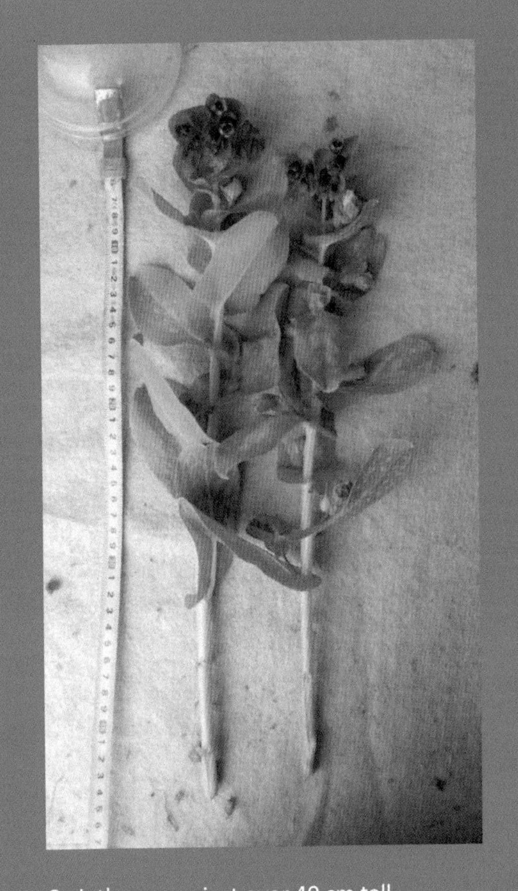

Cerinthe grows just over 40 cm tall.

Physostegia "Rose Queen"

Solidago "Ivory Glory"

maroon ("black") cornflowers: it's the traditional blue variety that the brides want. Make sure you hydrate cornflowers immediately after picking otherwise the unopened flower buds (of which there are always a lot!) will start drooping. In the vase with flower food the buds will open and the vase life is actually quite good, even though individual flowers will perish within four to five days.

Recommended varieties: "Blue Boy"

Physostegia

Physostegia is also known as the "Obedient Flower" because of the unusual charcteristic that the individual florets on the spikes are hinged, and can be bent in a particular position where they will remain... Physostegia can easily be grown from seed but will not flower until its second year. The white varieties seem much weaker than the pink varieties, which are very strong, nearly two metres tall and very productive! The downside is that physostegia has a relatively short harvesting window of three to four weeks, during which time the grower needs to familiarise the florists with this crop.

Recommended varieties: "Rose Queen"

Sedum

Sedum is not the most popular filler in the shop, but most florists will buy some as part of a bigger order. It is very easy to propagate, even leaf cuttings root within four weeks. Some modern varieties are PBR-protected and should not be propagated without a licence.

Recommended varieties: "Matrona", "Autumn Joy" ("Herbstfreude")

Solidago

Goldenrod is a real floristry jack-of-all-trades; it is produced in huge quantities overseas and the price is low. Being yellow-flowered it is not the hottest bloom in town at the moment, but now there is an ivory-coloured variety which you could try. All solidago is harvested when still in the bud. Even though solidago is a perennial, we don't grow it in landscape fabric so that it can spread and provide us with many more stems over time.

Recommended varieties: "Ivory Glory" (Danziger, Israel)

Stachys

This is my personal discovery of the decade! Lamb's Ear forms statuesque furry flower stems with the tactile appeal of rich velvet. To be harvested before the little pink flowers appear (they turn brown quickly) these amazing stems last easily three weeks in the vase.

Most florists will be familiar with freeze-dried stachys leaves which they can buy for use in fancy wedding work (buttonholes etc). The stems are not a common floristry line, but when a florist has bought them once, they are totally hooked and will show withdrawal symptoms once the season is over! Extremely popular. Harvest is early in the season when there isn't so much else.

Stachys is mostly grown from seed, but there is one named variety which has bigger leaves and taller stems and can be vegetatively propagated through divisions.

Recommended varieties: "Big Ears", the species

Stachys (Lamb's Ear) has turned out to be a very popular filler.

A trolley full of stachys.

Special interest fillers

Lunaria

Honesty is a biennial, and is grown for the stems with the green seedpods. The seedpods can be dried as well.

Rubus

Especially late in the season there is a market for thornless raspberries and blackberries for autumnal arrangements. Make sure the fruits aren't so ripe that they fall off – causing nasty stains on table cloths.

You could also try Japanese wineberry (rubus phoenicolasius), the stems are quite thorny but more decorative than raspberries and blackberries.

Apple mint grown in landscape fabric

Eucalyptus gunnii can be grown in landscape fabric on a relatively tight planting distance (here 30 by 30 cm)

Foliage

The term foliage refers to stems with only leaves, and it adds a natural look to the bouquet.

Top foliage

Apple mint

Easy to grow and easy to propagate through root cuttings or divisions, apple mint is a scented bright green foliage plant.

Asparagus

Often sold as "asparagus fern", which isn't a fern at all! You can grow asparagus plants from seeds and there is no need to splash out on special varieties for asparagus vegetable production – in fact any variety will do. It might be worth experimenting with purple asparagus... Asparagus foliage has a long vase life and looks great in bouquets.

Recommended varieties: "Connover's Colossal", "Smilax"

Bupleurum griffithii

Bupleurum is a well-known line for florists and wholesalers – it looks like eucalyptus but is grown as an annual. It germinates and grows easily and it is a very suitable crop for British growers. Unfortunately no breeding has gone into this crop so there is only the species to grow.

Eucalyptus

Widely used and very popular, it needs to be cut relatively late in the season when the stems have firmed up sufficiently to prevent drooping. Often the tips are pinched out as they often droop anyhow. Eucalyptus is a fast-growing shrub or tree which needs to be kept small otherwise it might overgrow your garden. In a research project done in Northern Ireland the trees were pruned in March to a height of 1.20 metres; personally I use a system of coppicing at 20 cm height. The Northern Irish researchers recommend a spacing of 2 metres between the rows and 2 metres in the row; at Wealden Flowers we grow eucalyptus gunnii in a 30 by 30 cm pattern.

Eucalyptus can easily be established from seeds (cropping starts in second year) and it can be grown successfully in landscape fabric to prevent weed growth.

Recommended varieties: Eucalyptus gunnii, Eucalyptus parvifolia

Physocarpus opulifolium

This is a landscape shrub from the USA, with lovely viburnum-like foliage. The variety "Diablo" has red foliage and is very vigorous, resulting in many sellable stems every year. This variety is PBR-protected and royalties need to be paid for propagation. Propagation itself is easy, especially when rooting cuttings in a mist unit with bottom heat in July and August.

Recommended varieties: "Diablo"

Worth trying foliage

Basil

Ornamental varieties of basil have been developed, but just as the edible varieties they thrive best in a greenhouse or polytunnel.

Recommended varieties: "Cardinal" (Genesis Seeds, available through Tamar Organics)

Pittosporum

Pittosporum is grown on a large scale in Cornwall, and production in other areas depends on the local microclimate.

Salal

Salal is grown in the North, and is actually the green leafy stem of Gaultheria shallon. Salal is a member of the heather family and thrives in acid soils.

Special interest foliage

Ivy, holly

Christmas specials ivy and holly – usually foraged in the wild...

Hops

Hops can be grown on trellises; in the olden days on 10 metre high ones in Kent! Hops have separate male and female plants, and the females are the best for the decorative flowers. There might be a good market for its long trailing stems with leaves and flowers to decorate churches and marquees for autumnal weddings.

Senecio greyii

This is a relatively short stemmed shrub with grey silvery leaves which have the benefit of not curling up when made into buttonholes. Senecio is very easy to propagate from stem cuttings, and it is a good idea to have some bushes in a hedge or a sheltered spot.

Lovely wreath based on lamb's ear (stachys) with autumnal flowers such as dahlia "Maarten Zwaan", echinacea and some elder berries.

The winter

As you can see from the "Cut Flower Planner" poster (appendix), most crops are ready to harvest between June and September. You will already have stopped harvesting sweet peas by mid-August the latest, as their stems will have become so short that they won't be useable any more. Mildew sets in, and it's best to clear the sweet peas away altogether. As soon as the first frosts start, the tender annuals, like zinnias and sunflowers, will give up. The roses will still continue to produce good quality flowers for a while, but production is certainly in decline.

Christmas is a peak time for markets, think of Advents and Christmas fairs in many towns and villages – but it is a difficult time to produce any flowers, unless you have a heated greenhouse and can produce stocks, chrysanths or antirrhinums.

Chrysanths

The culture of chrysanthemums was traditionally carried out as follows: in spring the chrysanthemum cuttings were taken and rooted. In early summer the plants would be potted up in big pots, and grown on over the summer period outside. They were 'stopped' (pinched) at various stages, and when the greenhouses were cleared of the summer crops (tomato or ornamental crops), the chrysanthemum pots would be brought inside before the first frosts would hit them. With a little bit of heat the chrysanthemums could be forced into bloom by Christmas.

Woody stems

Without a heated greenhouse, you are limited as to what you can harvest from outside at that time of the year, which includes a lot of leafless winter stems, such as curly hazel, curly willow (and other types of willow), red dogwood, etc. You might also be able to harvest from the wild; holly and ivy are much in demand around Yuletide. Ask the landowner for permission!

Forsythsia can be cut when still in tight bud and forced into flower in a warm room or greenhouse. Pity they only come in yellow – they are not very popular at all, however there is also a white forsythsia called abeliophyllum distichum which has a lot more potential.

Helleborus

Hellebores are one of the first flowers to bloom in spring - they start flowering from February onwards. There is a lot of breeding happening in helleborus at the moment, and some fascinating varieties have appeared on the market: amazing doubles and fantastic new colours. Hellebores need to be picked when the flowers are very mature (stamens have dropped, seedpod starts to form) otherwise vaselife will be very poor. Maturely picked flowers can last very long in the vase.

Potted bulbs

There may be a good market for potted bulbs (dwarf narcissi, muscari, tulips, etc), especially if you use some special vintage pots and add some moss or winter twigs.

Calculations

For all crops you grow you will have to calculate how many plants you need, and how much space these plants will take up in your garden. Some crops are grown close together on a very narrow spacing, such as stocks. Other (bigger) plants need more space, such as roses and sunflowers.

Usually in production situations, we grow our crops in beds. A bed is defined as the growing space between the two paths that mark the boundaries of a bed. If you work with a tractor the paths will be made by the tractor tyres, and the bed width is determined by the track width of the tractor. The track width of a tractor can be adjusted by swapping the tyres around, and can be increased with most small tractors from 1.20 metres to 1.75 metres. We determine the ***track width*** of a tractor by measuring the distance from the centre of the left tyre to the centre of the right tyre.

The ***bed width*** is the actual area between the tyres, so without the tracks. If you work with a tractor, the bed width depends on the track width of the tractor and the width of the tyres. If your tractor has a track width of 1.50 metres and the tyres are 30cm wide, the bed width will be 1.20 metres (see picture).

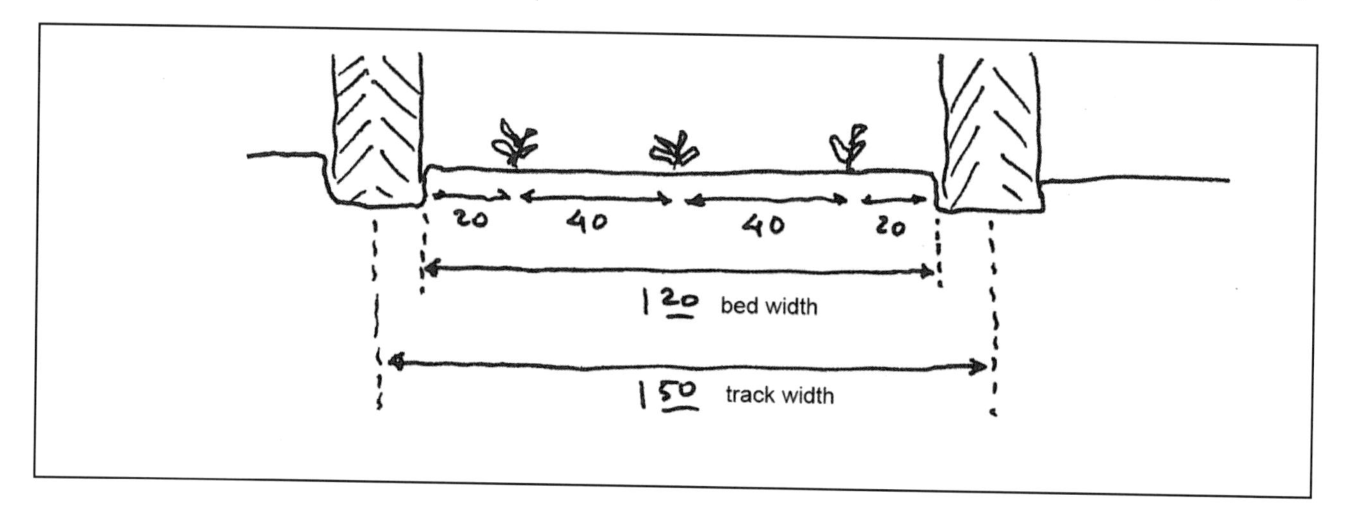

How many rows per bed

Once you know the bed width, you can work out for your crop how many rows fit in the bed. On a 1.20 metre wide bed you can fit 3 rows of a crop with a distance of 40cm between the rows (see picture). Alternatively you can fit 4 rows of a crop on such a bed if the distance between the rows is 30cm.

On a 1.00 metre wide bed you can fit 3 rows of crops with a distance of 30cm between the rows. This is the system we use at Wealden Flowers.

How many plants per row

After working out how many rows you can fit on a bed, you have to calculate how many plants you can fit in each row. For this you need to know the length of the beds and divide it by the spacing between the plants within the row.

$$number\ of\ plants\ per\ row = \frac{total\ length\ of\ the\ bed}{distance\ between\ each\ plant\ in\ the\ row}$$

Example for a bed which is 50 metres long and plants planted 30cm apart (30cm = 0.30 metre):

$$number\ of\ plants\ per\ row = \frac{50\ metres}{0.30\ metres} = 167\ plants\ per\ row$$

Note that you use the same unit (metre) for both the length of the bed and the distance between individual plants.

How many plants per bed

In order to work out the amount of plants you can plant on each bed you have to multiply the number of plants per row by the number of rows per bed.

Using the figures from the example above:

167 plants per row × 3 rows per bed ≈ 500 plants per bed.

Planning exercise Sunflowers

Scenario:

- You have beds of 25 metres each.
- You have 3 rows per bed, and you plant your sunflowers 30cm apart in the rows.
- You would like to produce 100 sunflowers every week from early July to early September.
- You sell the sunflowers for 60p each.

Questions:

- How many batches do you need to sow?
- How many plants do you need for each batch?
- Make a sowing plan for this project.
- How many beds do you need?
- How many seeds do you order?
- What is you revenue for this crop?

Answers:

- During the months of July and August, one batch will produce flowers for about 2 weeks. During September, one batch will last around 3-4 weeks. From this follows that we will need to sow two batches for July, two batches for August and one big batch for September.
- We would like 100 sunflowers per week. The batches in July and August will last for about two weeks, so we need to plant batches of 200 plants at the time. You will not harvest a useable flower from each and every plant, so you plant some extra. In this case I would recommend that you plant 25% extra, so instead of 200 plants, you plant 250 plants per batch in July and August. In September, your batch needs to cover 4 weeks instead of 2, so we need a bigger batch. For 4 weeks, we need 400 plants, but again we will allow for some spillage, so we plant 25% more: 500 plants.
- To create the sowing plan we consult the "Cut Flower Planner" poster, from which we can deduct the planting and sowing times for every harvest batch.

  Sowing plan:

Batch #	Sowing	Planting	Harvesting	Quantity
1	early April	late April	early July	250
2	late April	early May	late July	250
3	early May	late May	early August	250
4	late May	early June	late August	250
5	early June	late June	September	500

Our beds are 25 metres long, and they have 3 rows of sunflowers. We plant the sunflowers 30cm apart in the row. In one row of sunflowers we can fit:

$$number\ of\ plants\ per\ row = \frac{25\ metres}{0.30\ metres} = 83\ plants\ per\ row$$

We have 3 rows per bed, so that means we can plant 250 plants on every bed. We need a total of 1500 plants, so that equals 1500:250=6 beds of sunflowers.

- We need a total of 1500 plants, which already includes 25% extra for crop failure etc. As sunflower seeds have a nearly 100% germination rate, we will be fine with 1500 sunflower seeds.
- If we sell all sunflowers for 60p, this crop will give us a revenue of 1500 x 0.60 = £900.

Planning exercise Zinnia

Scenario:

- You have beds of 10 meters each.
- Your beds have 2 rows each, and you plant your zinnias 30 cm apart in the row.
- You would like to produce 50 stems of zinnia every week, from early July to late September.

Questions:

- How many batches do you need to sow?
- How many plants do you need for each batch?
- Make a sowing plan for this project.
- How many beds do you need?
- How many seeds do you order?

Answers:

- A batch of zinnias produces from early to late July all the way until the frost kills them, so one batch is sufficient.
- On average you can harvest 3 stems per plant, although it depends on soil fertility and how much sunshine there is in any given summer. If you want 50 stems per week for 13 weeks that equals 800 stems in total. 800 divided by 3 equals 270 plants – round up to 300 plants.
- Sow 300 plants in late April, plant them out in late May and start harvesting early to late July.
- Our beds are 25 metres long, and they have 3 rows of zinnias. We plant the zinnias 30cm apart in the row. In one row of zinnia we can fit:

  $$number\ of\ plants\ per\ row = \frac{25\ metres}{0.30\ metres} = 83\ plants\ per\ row$$

  We have 3 rows per bed, so that means we can plant 250 plants on every bed. We need a total of 300 plants, so that equals 300:250=1.2 beds of zinnias. In reality you would probably either plant 1 or 2 beds.
- For 1 bed we need 250 seeds, or for 2 beds we need 500 seeds.

Flower cultivation

Soil fertility and soil cultivation

A lot of the flower crops need quite a rich soil: the plants not only have to establish a root system and leaves (like most vegetables), but need enough vitality to also shoot and develop flowers. Well-supplied plants produce thicker stems, and thicker stems produce flowers which last longer in the vase. The key to a good vase life lies in providing the plants with all their nutritional needs. A lot of quality problems are the result of nutrient deficiencies in the soil, or lack of water during the growing season.

Soil testing

The first thing to do when you start growing flowers on a field of which you don't know the history, is to take soil samples and send them to a soil laboratory. As an organic grower I am interested in the living aspects of the soil as well as the chemical contents, so I send my samples to a specialist lab whose reports include not only macro and micro nutrients, but also cation exchange capacity and the amount of bacteria and fungi in the soil. Alternatively you can just send your sample to the local fertiliser supplier and they will be able to supply a report with the amounts of N, P and K, and liming needs. Not quite as useful but good for starters.

Good organic inputs to raise the fertility and the organic matter content of your soil include farm yard manure (FYM), horse manure, and different types of compost. Greenwaste compost can be bought from council composting sites across the country, and even though the nutritive value is very limited it provides abundant organic matter to your soil.

Perennials: mycorrhizae

Healthy, organically managed farm soil contains a lot of soil bacteria. Bacteria are very efficient in breaking down organic matter and making their nutrients available to the plants. Fungi are even more effective in breaking down hard-to-digest organic matter and making recalcitrant nutrients such as phosphate available to plants. Almost all plants will engage in mycorrhizal symbiosis given the chance: this means that a soil fungus will work together with the plant roots in a mutually beneficial relationship in which the plant feeds the fungus with sugars, and the fungus provides the plant with certain nutrients and water. Unfortunately fungi are killed by repeated cultivation, but in our fields with perennials there is a great opportunity to establish a multitude of mycorrhizal associations, thus making your perennials much more resilient against water and nutrient stress. You can buy beneficial fungi in garden centres under the brand name Rootgrow™ which you then apply once at planting time. These beneficial fungi go on to create a second root system to your plants, which increases their ability to take up water and nutrients more than a hundred-fold.

Feeding perennials, especially when grown in a ground cover like Mypex™, is a bit complicated as you can't add any composts or manures. It is therefore crucial that you give your perennials a good start in a soil to which you have added a generous amount of organic matter, ideally a good compost. Greenwaste compost from the councils is a good and affordable source of organic material. If after a few years you need to add fertility, you can do that through sprinkling some organic chicken manure pellets through the planting holes, ideally in spring before there are too many leaves in the way, or by using liquid fertilisers. There are even organically approved liquid fertilisers on the market, one brand is Plant Health Care. You can mix these products in with your irrigation water and feed them through the dripline of your irrigation system. Most people would use a fertiliser injector which saves you the hassle and the need for a big mixing basin – Dosatron is a well-known brand of fertiliser injectors.

Annuals: crop rotation

For annuals you can use a crop rotation: a system whereby plots with fertility builders (green manures such as clovers, trefoils and alfalfa – all of which fix nitrogen from the air) are followed by heavy feeding crops such as sunflowers, antirrhinums, amaranthus and zinnias, which are then followed by medium feeders such as bupleurum, molucella and clary sage, which in turn are being followed by crops that will thrive on relatively modest fertility such as ammi, dill and other members of the umbelliferae family. After this last group of crops you sow a green manure to start the fertility cycle again, increasing the levels of nitrogen through natural fixation. You will still have to incorporate sources of other nutrients – organic chicken manure pellets can be used, or any of the animal manures or composts. You would apply these right after incorporating the green manure so that the heavy feeders have all they need to produce a good crop.

Soil cultivation

The fields where you grow your annuals will have to be cultivated regularly in order to prepare beds for sowing or planting. Most growers use a muck spreader to spread the compost or manure, and afterwards plough the field to incorporate the fertility and the old crop residues and weeds. It is important to start with a nice 'clean' field, free of weeds and crop debris. The next cultivation involves the actual creation of a 'seedbed' which depending on your soil type can be done with a cultivator (light soils) or a rotavator (medium to heavier soils). This secondary cultivation leaves a nice flat crumbly soil surface into which you can drill or plant your crops.

Arjen using a small hand-held rotavator to prepare a seedbed in the greenhouse.

Direct drilling or transplants?

There are two ways of establishing your annual crops: either you sow your crops directly in the field in the spot where you want them to grow, or you plant seedlings which you have raised in a greenhouse or bought from a nursery. Since specialist flower seeds are rather expensive, and directly drilled crops can be prone to slug, bird and frost attack, I always start with transplants of pretty much everything I grow. I produce most of my own transplants, but because my greenhouse isn't big enough I supplement with bought-in plugs from an organic plant nursery. You can send them your seeds and they will happily produce the transplants for you, often for a very competitive price compared to doing it yourself. Be aware though that most plant nurseries are not familiar with the crops you are growing, and they might be struggling to germinate your seeds or to deal with pests that they are unfamiliar with. If they fail to raise sufficient plants for you, you are in serious trouble as you won't have the starting material to plant up your garden and grow your flowers. After having experienced this situation myself, during a year where more than half of the transplants I ordered from the nursery failed to materialise, I recommend that you try everything you can to propagate your own seedlings.

Facilities for propagation from seed

For seedling production you need a small greenhouse or polytunnel which you can keep frost free, for example with a little electric heater. In the greenhouse you need benches to put your seedling trays on, to keep them away from slugs and mice. You will need mains electricity for an electric heater, and it is very useful for your own nursery bed with bottom heat, which speeds up germination of most crops. I always water my seedlings by hand, so I can keep a close tab on how wet or dry the plug trays are – automatic irrigation systems often have a tendency to either flood your plants or to give an uneven coverage resulting in dry patches of miserable plants.

Plug trays in three sizes: 600 cells, 345 cells and 126 cells. Three trays fit exactly on our filling bench, where the vertical sides prevent potting soil from spilling when we fill the trays.

Plug trays

You can grow transplants in flimsy single use plug trays, or you can invest in the sturdy long-life type. I prefer the rigid ones which last forever so you

A so-called blocking tray with a 126 cell plug tray. Now trays can be stacked for internal transport to the field without crushing any seedlings.

The blocking trays are also very useful for holding 54 square 7cm pots, which we use a lot in the propagation of perennials and shrubs.

only need to buy them once – it is useful to include an ejector board with your purchase, this is a board with a large number of pins corresponding to the holes in the bottoms of your plug cells and it helps greatly with popping your plants out of the cells before you plant them. Plug trays come in many different sizes – the type I am using is 400 by 600mm outer dimensions and comes in 126 cell, 216 cell, 300 cell and 600 cell versions. The 600 cell plugs are tiny which means that your plants have very little reserve food and water so you really need to monitor them closely and regularly irrigate and possibly supply them with a liquid feed. I mainly use the 126 cell version which has relatively big cells (60cc) which means that we don't need to get stressed when we can't plant them out in time as they will be well supplied with potting soil and nutrients until they're quite big. We use some 600 cell plug trays too, which have only 15cc cells and you can often see the effect on the plants – they look a bit yellow and starved if you don't liquid feed them in time. The benefit of 300 or 600 cell plug trays is the efficient use of both seedling compost as well as (heated) greenhouse space: with the 126 cell trays you can only grow 500 plants per square metre, but if you use the 300 cell trays that increases to 1250 and using the 600 cell trays you grow 2500 plants on every square metre, using a similar amount of seedling compost...

For internal transport and stacking you can buy so called "blocking trays", into which a 400 x 600mm plug tray exactly fits. These blocking trays are designed in such a way that they can be stacked neatly on top of each other without crushing the seedlings in the plug trays.

Seedling compost

There are many different types and brands of seedling compost on the market. The most important aspects of a good seedling compost are that it holds moisture well, contains adequate fertility and that every time you buy it, it has the same consistently good quality. Especially the last aspect is a difficult one, and I have seen many batches of seedlings go to ruin because the seedling compost was not good enough. When you spend a lot of money on seeds, electricity, water and a lot of love and care to produce the foundation of your productive year you have to be able to rely on consistently good seedling compost to give your crops the best start in life. I have used many brands and types of potting soil and have decided to buy only one brand which is organic, holds moisture well, keeps the plants well-supplied with nutrients and is consistently good. Klasmann-Deilmann is probably the biggest potting soil producer in Europe and for a good reason: they produce top quality material. They have an excellent organic range and are reducing peat content by up to 40%. In a recent survey among members of the Organic Growers Alliance Klasmann-Deilmann also came out as the best and most trusted seedling compost.

Protection

It is good practice to cover your seeds with vermiculite after sowing. Vermiculite is made from clay which has been subjected to a very high temperature which makes it pop like popcorn. It comes in two grades: medium and fine. The fine material provides perfect conditions for seeds to germinate under, and keeps the surface dry which prevents moss and algal growth. Since using vermiculite I have never had any problems any more with pythium, a fungal disease which kills germinating seedlings, especially in moist conditions.

Mice and voles can be a serious problem, so it is good practice to place some mouse traps strategically around your seedling trays. One mouse or vole can destroy a whole tray of sweet pea seedlings within a night, so don't be too tender-hearted and get the mouse traps out. I use peanut butter as a bait and chocolate works very well too. It's anyway advisable to have some chocolate handy for emergencies!

Planting out

When your transplants have grown two to three true leaves it is time to plant them out. Except on really large scale operations most flower growers plant out their seedlings by hand. It is good practice to create beds with a fixed number of rows, with a standard distance between the rows. I use 1.10m beds with three rows of plants 30 cm (= 300 mm) apart. You will need a row marker to mark the rows on your beds, so that the rows are always parallel to each other – which will make subsequent weeding and hoeing a lot easier. If you're handy, you can weld a row marker together yourself and fix it permanently behind your rotavator saving you an extra pass with the tractor. For planting out we work on our knees: place the crate of transplants on your left in the track, and dig the holes with your right hand while your left hand picks up the transplants one by one and plants them in the holes. After a while you get really efficient and fast at doing this, and the trick is to make it as comfortable as possible: make sure you are wearing trousers with knee pockets and really comfy knee protectors. If the soil is moist, make sure you have good waterproof trousers – the bib-and-brace (dungaree) type doesn't get stripped off your bottom as you crawl over your fields...

Facilities for vegetative propagation

All annuals and several perennials can easily be grown from seeds, but all shrubs and quite a number of perennials are much better propagated vegetatively. The two main types of vegetative propagation for cut flower growers are divisions and cuttings.

Propagation bed under construction: the raised bed is covered with landscape fabric to prevent weeds from penetrating from below. An electric soil warming cable has been zig-zagged on the fabric and the bed is being covered with a mixture of peat and coarse sand (2:1). Dolomitic lime has been added to correct the pH.

Above the bed the mist nozzles can be seen.

Cuttings in the process of rooting...

A lot of perennials can be divided. You need a strong and big mother plant, which can be from your garden or one that you buy from a nursery. I have sometimes managed to make more than 30 divisions from one single rudbeckia plant from a local nursery – so that was eight pounds well spent. You dig the plant up or you take it out of the pot it came in, and divide the clump into several small partitions, each with a piece of root and some buds or shoots. The best time to do this is in spring, when the buds are just starting to sprout.

Many shrubs useful for cutting can be propagated by taking cuttings. Most cuttings root in 4-8 weeks, especially in a propagating bed with bottom heat and automatic mist irrigation. You can buy ready-made units starting from around £500 or you can create your own by using a soil warming cable (£30) and a mist irrigation kit (£250). The advantage of the DIY version is that you can expand it as your needs increase by adding mist nozzles to the system. You can grow around 500 shrub cuttings per square metre at a time. I have successfully used the DIY system to root cuttings of hydrangea, symphoricarpos, deutzia, caryopteris, viburnum, hypericum and physocarpus. Most rooted cuttings ("liners") cost between £1 and £2 when you buy them from a large trade nursery, but you can buy unrooted cuttings for as little as 10p, so there is a great potential here to save (or even make) some money. Buying from your local retail nursery is the most expensive option, they will easily charge between £5 and £10 for the same rooted cutting, potted up in a plastic pot with a nice label.

Dealing with weeds

Generally speaking, there are two different types of weeds: annual weeds and perennial weeds. The annual type grows from seeds and germinates really quickly and can grow explosively. Annual weeds can completely cover a bare patch of land within 4 weeks. Good examples of annual weeds are chickweed, fat hen and redshank.

The perennial weeds grow from a perennial rootstock and keep coming back year after year – famous examples are docks, bindweed and couchgrass. The more you rotavate, the more you propagate this type of weeds, so you need to be careful with how you deal with perennial weeds.

Annual weeds

The annual weeds can usually be dealt with relatively easily by regular weeding and hand hoeing. I am a great fan of the Dutch hoe; a small Dutch company called Sneeboer makes an excellent hand-forged stainless steel Dutch hoe. As long as you get the annual weeds at a young stage, they can be easily hoed off their roots after which they die. They don't grow back from their root system.

Lilac freshly planted in landscape fabric.

Perennial weeds

The perennial weeds are much trickier to deal with, and ultimately always involve some way of getting the roots out of the ground. There are very good tools to pull up dock roots, we have good experience with tools from the Lazy Dog company. You can also use a tractor and dedicate several weeks of dry weather to regularly dragging out couchgrass or bindweed roots by racing over your field with a cultivator attached.

Landscape fabric

If you are growing perennials and shrubs, the best form of weed control is the use of landscape fabric. This is often known under the brand name Mypex™, but there are other brands such as Supacover™ etc. The ground fabric is a black plastic mulch which suppresses all growth underneath. With a plumber's torch you can burn holes in the fabric to plant the crop through. Burning holes is better than using a knife, as the torch seals the edges automatically which prevents the polythene from fraying. It's also faster. Almost all perennials can be grown through Mypex™, and in my experience it saves an enormous amount of work.

Good example of "competition growing": the stachys on the left grew among a taller crop (euphorbia) and the stems on the right grew without any competition. The difference is about 10 cm.

Competition growing

Some crops really benefit from a little competition for light and space, and will grow much straighter and taller when grown between fast-growing tall crops. If you grow stachys (lamb's ear) between two rows of euphorbia, you will get lovely tall straight stems of these velvety stems, whereas on their own they always grow bendy and relatively short. Other candidates include alchemilla mollis and apple mint.

Good examples of well-competing crops (fast growing, straight and relatively tall) are euphorbia, physostegia, solidago, hypericum and eryngium – all of which could be grown through landscape fabric in alternate rows with the crops that would benefit from some competition.

Protection

Unfortunately there is a whole host of nasty creatures that like your lovely flowers just as much as you do, except they want them for breakfast! Slugs, rabbits, deer and pigeons all have cut flower crops on the menu, and it can be a real challenge to protect your plants from their voracious appetite.

Slugs

There is no country in the world where slugs are such a problem as in Britain. In European countries like Holland or Germany growers will find a few slugs around the edges of their fields, along the grass strips, but such a complete full-scale assault as the British slugs manage to carry out is unheard of on the continent. Nowhere else provide the cool damp summers and the relatively warm wet winters such ideal conditions for continuous activity, breeding and feeding. There are three main species of slugs which cause most of the damage: the field slug, the garden slug and the keel slug. These troublesome creatures live underground and come to the surface to feed during the night, especially during moist conditions (which is almost every night in the UK). Traditional remedies such as beer traps or copper rings are not effective on a field scale, and the only product that really works is slug pellets. Luckily in recent years an organically approved slug pellet has arrived on the market, which is based on ferric phosphate, and is accepted by all organic certification bodies. This slug pellet, which is marketed under the brand names Ferramol and Sluxx, breaks down into iron and phosphate ions – two nutrients for our crops and this product is totally harmless to all other organisms in and above the ground. These slug pellets work at least as good – or better – than much more poisonous chemicals such as metaldehyde and methiocarb which are not allowed under organic certification and can cause problems for the drinking water companies (metaldehyde) and can kill pets like cats.

Rabbits

Rabbits can graze off whole beds of crops within one night – I once had a very promising stand of eryngium which they finished off before I could get the electric fence in place. A multi-pronged approach is asked for, don't rely on just one barrier! We use a rabbit fence around the whole field, but they have eaten holes through it and buried tunnels underneath. We use a portable electric wire which keeps them off the crops pretty well – as long as the battery is full. And then I usually cover newly planted seedlings with fleece as well, as an extra protection against the rabbits. My son gets paid for every rabbit he snares, and we have a good relationship with a local hunter who comes on a regular basis to practice his skills. And even with all these measures, we still lose a crop every now and again!

Deer

We are fortunate not to have a deer problem, although the forest near our fields is full of them, so we keep a close eye on them. The only thing that really keeps deer away is a proper deer fence – which is an expensive outlay, but when well-made should also keep the rabbits out. All in all, it pays to have a good quality fence around your field and I understand now why walled gardens were once so popular in Britain!

Frost

Tender annuals need to be protected from frost, and all crops grow better when protected in spring by a layer of fleece. Fleece is a thin blanket, made of polypropylene, which acts as an insulating layer over the crop resulting in up to three degrees frost protection. There are two types of fleece: the standard fleece which is 17 grams per square meter, and the so called winter fleece, which weighs 30 grams per square meter. Winter fleece lets less light through and is more expensive, and in most cases ordinary fleece will do the job well. Fleece doesn't have such a long life, after three or four years it is usually so ripped and torn that you have to replace it. There is fleece on the market with reinforced sides, which apparently lasts a bit longer – however a dog running through your fleece, or rabbits digging through it will ruin that type of fleece as well.

You spread the fleece over your crop and bury the sides at regular intervals by making holes with a spade and covering the edge of the fleece with the dug up soil. Some growers use sand bags or milk bottles filled with sand to keep their fleece in place.

Support

Tall flowering plants need support to keep them upright in windy conditions. Antirrhinums, eryngiums and hydrangeas are examples of crops that need support netting in our fields. The Dutch have developed a clever system of support posts onto which they lay a galvanised net horizontally. The advantage of this system is that you can easily raise the net as the crop grows taller, and if you want you can use a second layer of net above the first layer. You can also create your own system with stock fencing mesh and wooden posts.

Climbing crops such as sweet peas, clematis, hops and trachelospermum need to be tied to a vertical support. For sweet peas we use vertical support netting, as we don't practice cordon culture. If you grow sweet peas as a cordon you would use single lengths of string – one for each plant. We grow our sweet peas "naturally" which means that we don't prune them, but we do help them along the support netting, using a special tying tool

Horizontal support netting in use in a bed of hydrangea "Annabelle".

A Max Tapener tying tool is a useful piece of equipment to tie sweet pea stems to stakes and netting.

called a Max Tapener. With the Max Tapener you can tie your climbers to the netting very fast and efficiently, preventing them from falling over and producing bent stems.

Irrigation

On light soils you will certainly need an irrigation system, and even on heavier soils it is highly recommended. A sandy soil dries out very quickly, and as long as your plants haven't been well established with deep roots, they will be highly susceptible to droughts. Especially recently planted crops often need extra water to get them through dry periods.

There are two types of irrigation: sprinkler systems and drip tape based. A sprinkler system will spread water over a whole area (several beds, or even a whole field) and is not nearly as efficient with water as a drip-based system. Drip tape is a type of hose with holes punched in them, through which water gets delivered close to the crop in small quantities at a time. Drip irrigation is very efficient with water and is highly recommended by the water companies. The downside of drip irrigation is that you need to put down a lot of pipes (drip tape) and once there, they get in the way when you are hoeing. Drip tape is very useful in perennial crops, where you can leave it in place either above or underneath the polythene ground cover. If you use a durable type rather than the thin-walled products, they should last for the life of your perennials and possibly longer. We use Techline™ from the well-known Israeli company Netafim™, which is a sturdy durable drip tape. Every hole in the drip tape has its own little pressure regulator, which means that the holes closest to the pump release the same amount of water per hour as the ones right at the end of the drip line. This is essential if you want an equal distribution of water.

The source of your water can be mains, a river or a borehole. Mains water is expensive and you need to make sure you really use your water efficiently. Pumping water from a river or a borehole costs money to fuel the pump (either petrol, diesel or electricity) but apart from that it is free up to currently 20 cubic metres of water per day – above that you will need to buy an abstraction licence. For more information about water abstraction check the website of the Environment Agency.

Greenhouses and polytunnels

The British climate is not very gentle on all our flower crops, and several crops thrive much better under the protection of a greenhouse or polytunnel. Greenhouses and polytunnels give protection from cold, wind, insects and rain, and can be a godsend in wet and cold summers. Not every crop needs all the different forms of protection, sweet peas for example don't necessarily need the protection against the cold but will reliably produce a much better quality crop when not exposed to the rain. Insects such as flea beetles can create havoc in outdoor grown stocks, and antirrhinums can be brought to flower much earlier in the season when grown indoors.

Greenhouses

A greenhouse is the best structure for your crops: it is durable and usually has a fairly large air volume which means less temperature fluctuation than in a polytunnel. They are pleasant to work in, often easier to ventilate with roof ventilation. Warm air rises naturally, so by opening the roof windows you automatically get a natural air flow which reduces moisture build-up in the greenhouse. Too much moisture creates conditions for fungal diseases, so good ventilation is essential. The only downside of a greenhouse is its price – they are expensive to buy and build.

Polytunnels

That is why most growers opt for polytunnels. Polytunnels are simple steel structures, consisting of metal hoops covered with transparent polythene film. They come in different sizes but the most commonly used size by commercial growers is 8 metres wide and 20 or 30 metres long. There are versions with straight sides which allow you to work right up to the edge of the tunnel. Often there are large barn doors on both ends, as well as over-lintel ventilation – if you position your tunnels on a slight slope you will more easily have a natural airflow when you open the doors. Sometimes an electric fan is installed to maintain a certain temperature and to help reduce humidity.

Spanish tunnels

Another option is to use so called Spanish tunnels. These are even simpler constructions, resembling polytunnels, but lighter (and cheaper) in construction. The purpose of these tunnels is mainly to keep crops dry, so for certain flower crops they are ideal. The polythene film is pulled over the hoops every year in spring and stays on for about half the year. In autumn the polythene is being rolled up and put in the gutters, and the crops growing in the tunnels will experience the winter cold. These tunnels are used a lot for soft fruit production, but they are also very suitable for the production of roses, peonies and many other flower crops.

Greenhouse production

Transplant production in a small polytunnel

Production under Spanish tunnels

Harvest and Post-Harvest

Harvesting

Timing

Now comes the most satisfying part of the whole flower growing enterprise: the harvest! After months of sowing, planting, weeding and hoeing, finally you can reap the rewards of your efforts. The best time of the day to harvest flowers is in the morning, when the crops are still cool from the night. Wait until the dew has dried up, some petals can get badly damaged if they stick together while moist. You can start early with the foliage and the fillers, and wait until the sun has dried the bigger flowers before you start picking those. If early morning doesn't work for a particular reason, late afternoon is a good time to harvest your flowers as well: the stems will be full of assimilates (sugars) which will support a long vase life.

Stage of flower development

There is a lot of variation regarding the optimum stage of harvesting for the various cut flowers and foliage. Some flowers need to be harvested while still in bud, whereas with other crops the buds don't open in the vase so the stems need to be cut with completely open flowers. Other types of crops have several flowers on the same stem in a raceme (sweet peas) or a spike (antirrhinum, gladiolus) – often these are picked when one-third to half of the florets are open. In de appendices you will find a long list of the optimum harvest stage of many different cut flowers.

Determining the correct stage of development

The different flower development stages in sweet pea. Sweet peas would normally be harvested between stage 4 and 5 as most sweet peas would be used immediately in weddings etc. Stage 3 is acceptable as well; the other buds will open in the vase within the next few days.

Tools

A pair of secateurs is the tool of choice for harvesting most crops. We always use Felco 2 secateurs, which are not cheap but when cared for, last a lifetime. I have used cheaper products as well, and as the saying goes: "the bitterness of poor quality lingers long after the sweetness of cheap price is forgotten". Sweet peas and other delicate flowers can also be harvested with "snips" or needle-nose secateurs, small pointy clippers which allow you to cut the sweet pea stems as close as possible to the main stem.

For the flowers grown in the fields we use special narrow harvesting trolleys with a small detachable hammock in which the flowers are carefully laid after having been picked. At the packing shed the hammocks with the flowers can be lifted off the trolleys and an empty one hung in for the next round of harvesting while the first batch is being processed.

The different harvest stages of sweet pea

Stage 1: one bud just showing colour

Stage 2: several buds showing colour

Stage 3: one flowers opened

Stage 4: one flower opened and second flower just opening

Stage 5: all flowers open

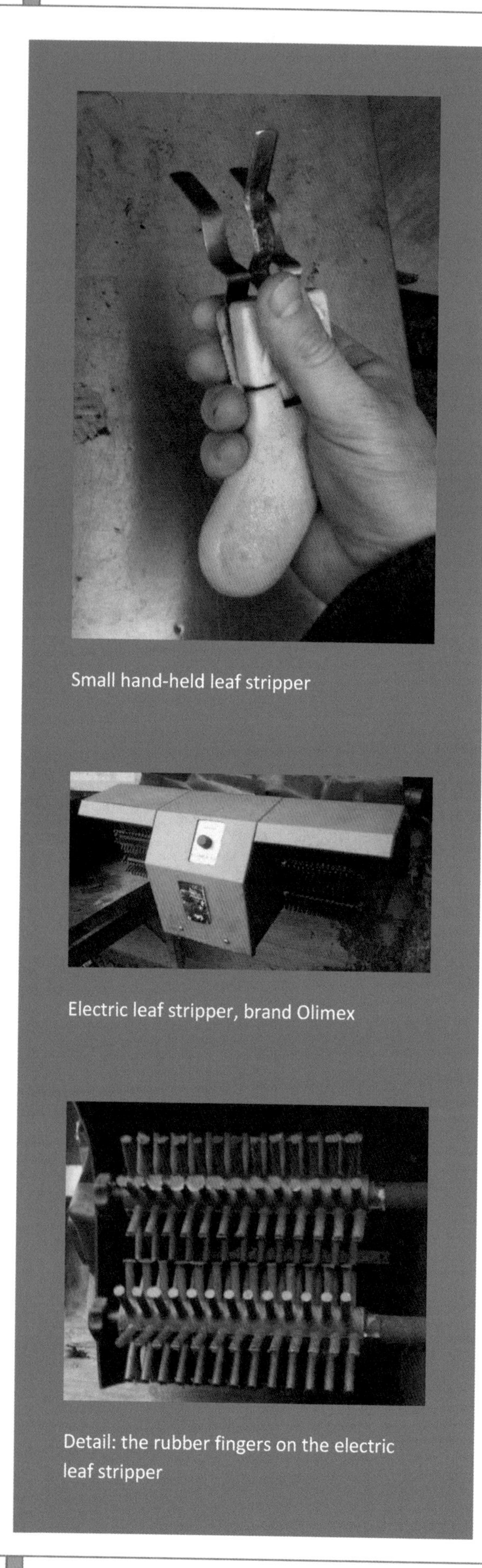

Small hand-held leaf stripper

Electric leaf stripper, brand Olimex

Detail: the rubber fingers on the electric leaf stripper

The harvesting trolleys we use are home-made. In the appendix you can find the building instructions of how to make them yourself.

How to harvest

Many crops will yield further stems if you don't cut them down at ground level: antirrhinums, scabiosa, zinnia and agastache for example will give useable side shoots – often somewhat thinner but still worthwhile. It is good practice to leave 2-5 nodes on the plant so that you can harvest side shoots later on.

Handling

When you come back to the shed with your bounty, it is time for post-harvest handling. There are several steps that we follow after picking: grading, stripping, bunching and sleeving, re-cutting, special treatments, hydrating, packing, cool storage and delivery. We'll go through them one by one.

Grading and sorting

Not all roses will have the same stem length, and not all antirrhinums will be equally thick, tall, open, etc. It is important to grade your stems, and reject the ones that don't meet the minimum standards. Assume the role of a really picky florist and be rigorous in what is acceptable and what isn't. There is enough bulk on the market, and it is a better strategy to try to build a reputation for quality – and that means everything that is too short, too bent, too thin, too open, too closed, too old, damaged or otherwise not up to standard needs to be graded out. Only top quality flowers and foliage goes to the customers. No shortcuts!

Stripping

Before bunching and sleeving, you have to strip the lower leaves off the stems. The leaves can contaminate the water significantly with bacteria and dirt. There are several tools on the market for stripping leaves: you can either just use your hand in a leather gardening glove, or you can buy a stripping pad from Chrysal. There are also small plastic stripping tools, but in my experience they don't last very long. Most florists in Holland have an electric leaf stripper in their shops, which is useful if you have to strip large quantities of stems, especially roses.

Bunching and sleeving

Bunching your flowers in bundles of 10 stems, and protecting them with a flower sleeve is good practice and makes your business look so much more professional. The additional benefit of sleeving your flowers lies in the fact that some flowers have a tendency to droop just after picking, but they will firm up again after rehydrating in the bucket. If they haven't been supported in the meantime, they will end up with firm but bent stems. The sleeve prevents that from happening – keeping your stems straight.

Re-cutting

When you cut the stems off the plants, the stems respond by sealing off the wound to prevent water losses. The cut ends on most flower stems will be sealed over within 30 minutes if not put in water. Most growers harvest their flower stems in harvest trolleys, picking a whole bed until the trolley is full before returning to the packing shed for further processing. During this time most of the stems will have sealed their ends, and it is important to re-cut the stems before they go into a hydrating solution.

Special treatments

Some flowers need a special treatment before hydrating, especially if they are ethylene sensitive. Ethylene is a natural gas that is emitted by ripening fruits but also by cut flower stems. Some flowers, such as sweet peas, larkspur and delphinium, react to ethylene in the atmosphere by dropping their petals. These flowers need to be pulsed in a solution containing silver thiosulphate (STS), which eliminates this response to ethylene. "Pulsing" means letting the flowers soak up this STS solution for a period of 4 to 72 hours. The solution stays at the farm, as the silver is a heavy metal and needs to be disposed of appropriately through a chemical waste depot. After pulsing in the STS solution the flowers are being sold in buckets containing the usual chlorine solution.

The silver thiosulphate solution can be used for up to a week. Be aware of the special requirements for disposal of this solution – see the Chrysal AVB label.

Hydrangea "Annabelle" 12 days after harvesting. The flowers on the left were untreated; the flowers on the right spent the first 24 hours in a solution with alum (aluminium sulphate) and the next 11 days in water with flower food (Chrysal Clear).

Zinnias after 8 days: the flowers on the left in tap water only; the flowers on the right were pretreated for 24 hours in Chrysal CVBn and subsequently were put in water with flower food (Chrysal Clear).

Untreated sweet peas after four days...

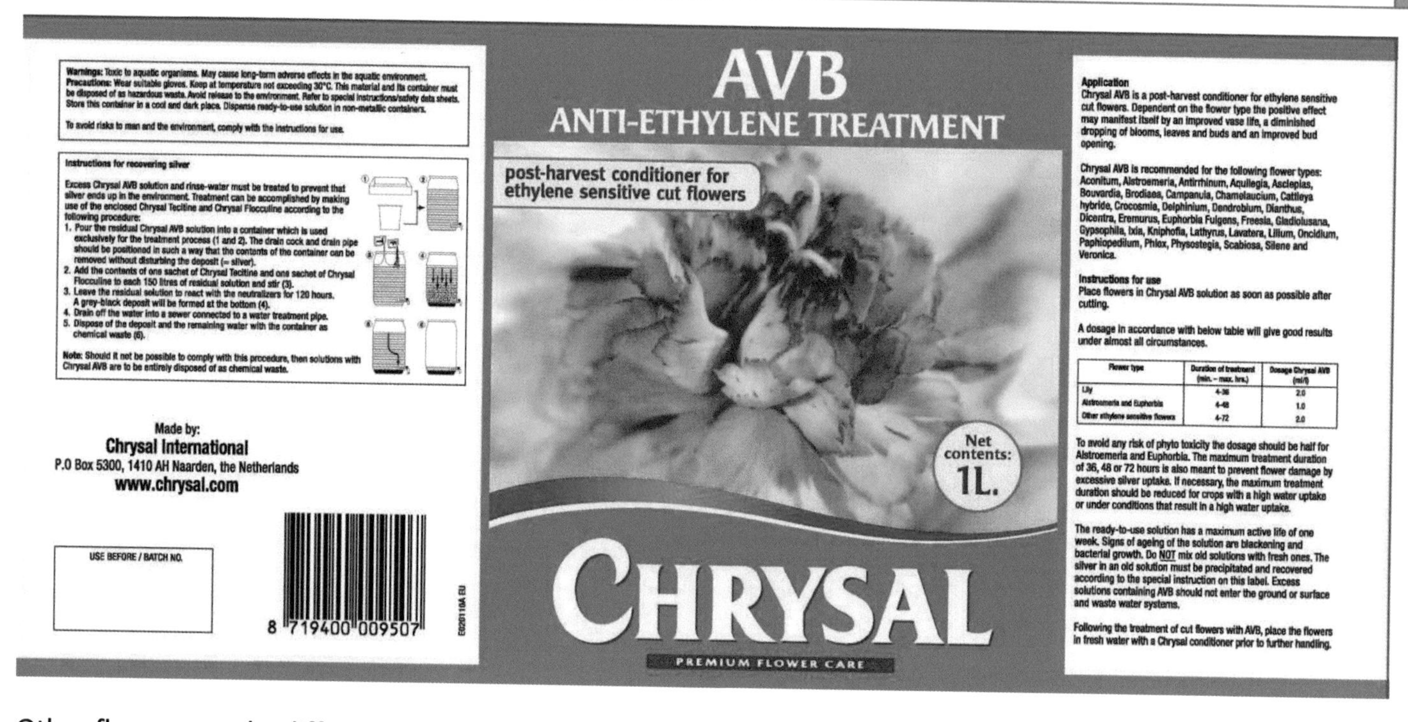

Other flowers need a different treatment: hydrangeas have a bad reputation for drooping shortly after harvest and being difficult to rehydrate. The solution to this is to dip the cut stems immediately in alum powder before putting them in a bucket with tap water (without hydrating solution!). Alum (aluminium sulphate) is a natural disinfectant and prevents the hydrangea stems from flopping over. Alum causes a chemical reaction with Chrysal CVBn, so don't mix the two products together.

Hydrating

The normal procedure for most crops is for the grower to place the flowers in a hydrating / holding solution. This solution contains a biocide, usually based on chlorine, thus preventing bacterial growth in the water. The grower sells the flowers in buckets containing this solution, and the florist then uses a different solution which contains flower food (sugars). By using these different treatments in the water the vaselife of the flowers is improved enormously.

The grower's product for hydrating is CVBn from Chrysal – this product comes as small white pills in a handy dispenser, like sweeteners for your coffee (not recommended). Each pill is designed to treat three litres of tap water, so it is important that you know how much water is in your buckets. If you install a toilet cistern in your packing shed, you can have an exact amount of water at a push of the button, in a very short time. This will save you time and you will always have the correct dosage of hydrating solution in your buckets.

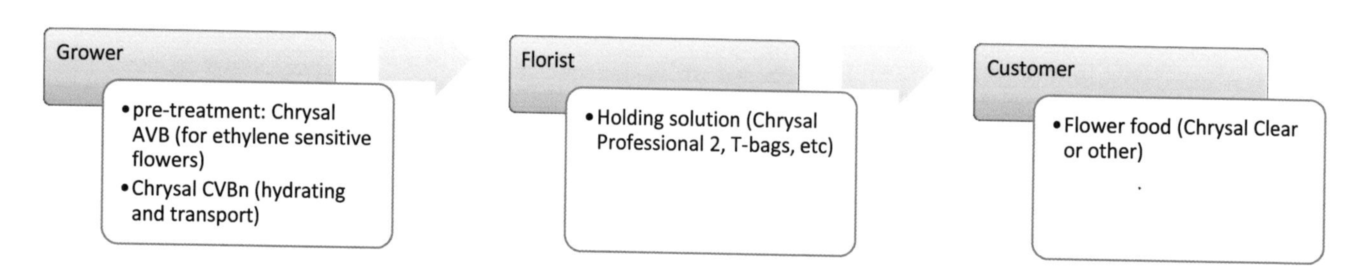

Packing

There are many different types of buckets you can choose from for your flowers: you can for example pick up used buckets from fish-and-chips shops and give them a good clean.

Flower wholesalers receive most of their flowers and foliage in returnable buckets from the Dutch auctions. These buckets carry an expensive deposit, so wholesalers will not be happy to give them to you although some might let you have them if you refund them the deposit. Strictly speaking this is illegal, as the buckets belong to the Dutch auction system and Dutch growers pay a fee for these buckets on top of the deposit every time they order clean ones from the auction group. Only growers who are members of the "bucket pool" are allowed to use these Dutch buckets.

A lot of flowers and foliage from Italy and other countries arrive at the wholesalers in non-returnable buckets – often fairly flimsy and cheap black plastic buckets, both round and square. It is these buckets that you can often pick up for free from the wholesalers, as they need to pay the waste-management companies to get rid of them – so they are usually happy for you to have them.

Whichever bucket you use: the most important thing is hygiene! Before you use any bucket for your flower crops, you need to make sure they are spotless and free from bacteria. Bacteria cause serious problems to your flower crops: they block the water conducting vessels (xylem) and cause premature wilting. Buy a bucket brush (equestrian shops) and a bottle of bleach (supermarket) and rinse and scrub your buckets with tap water with a little bit of bleach until they are so clean you could eat from them.

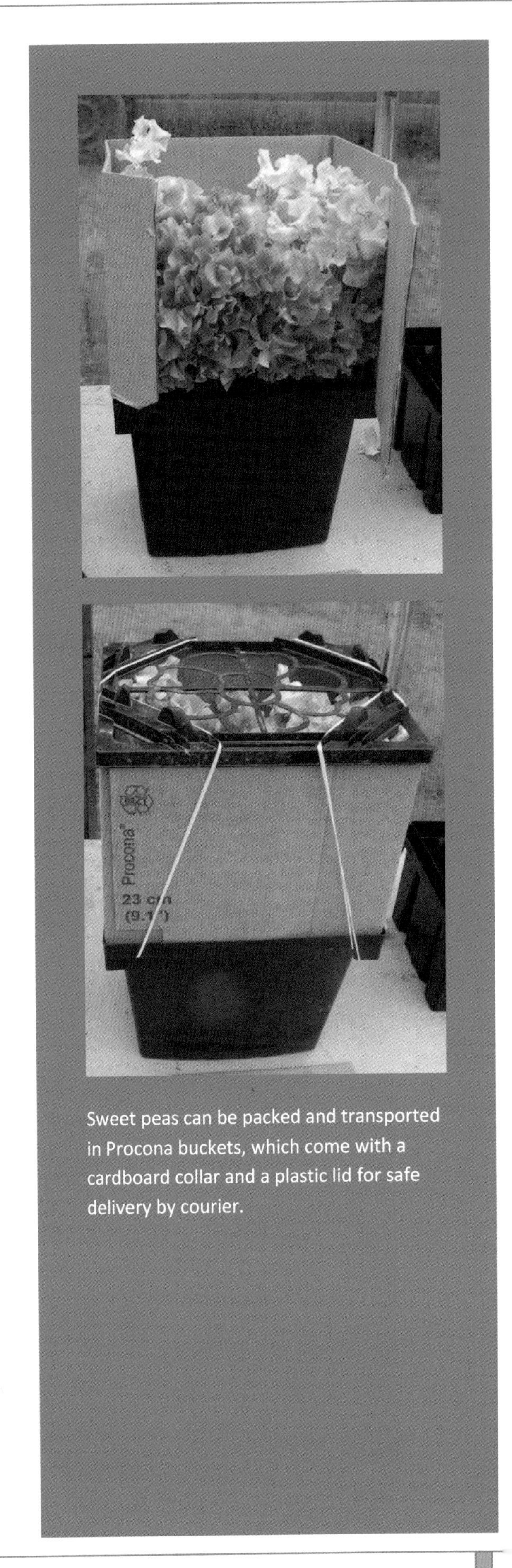

Sweet peas can be packed and transported in Procona buckets, which come with a cardboard collar and a plastic lid for safe delivery by courier.

Cool storage

In many books about cut flower production you will find the advice to make sure that there is an uninterrupted cold chain from grower to flower shop. If flowers are several days in transit, from tropical countries through airports and planes, warehouses and international road transport until they finally arrive in a British flower shop, then that is a sensible suggestion.

However, if flowers travel within a few hours from harvest straight to a flower shop, the temperature shock from being put in a cold store for half a day, and then out again, does not actually contribute to the flowers' vase life. It is much more sensible to keep the flowers in a cool spot (cool shed or in the shade) until you are ready to do the delivery rounds. You could consider investing in a refrigerated van and keep the thermostat at around 10-12 degrees, but in my experience this is all not needed in the UK. Harvest in the morning or in the evening, keep your flowers in a cool spot in a hydrating solution and deliver the next morning before the temperatures get too hot: that is the best procedure for maximising the vase life of your flowers.

If you are really keen to have refrigeration but are loath to spend thousands of pounds on a proper cold store, you could build a little super-insulated room and use a window-type air conditioning unit in combination with a CoolBot. The CoolBot is a little device that turns the air conditioning unit into a turbo-charged cooling machine at a fraction of the cost (both installation and energy use) of a real cold store. Find out more on www.storeitcold.com

Delivery

A white van or small truck is ideal, unless you have a very small operation and your family car is big enough. Even the most careful driver will have buckets flying through the van so you need a system to keep the buckets in place and upright. One option is to get fixed shelving with holes in which the buckets neatly fit; another option is to buy aluminium greenhouse shelving which you put in the van when needed, and can easily be taken out when you need the van to transport seedlings to your field. I am a great fan of this aluminium greenhouse shelving system, it keeps my van flexible and it is put in place or removed in just a few seconds.

Aluminium greenhouse shelving in use in a Toyota HiAce Powervan.

Financial and Business

Growing flowers is a fantastic pastime, but in the end most growers want to earn a living so we need to make sure that income exceeds expenditure. This part of the Cut Flower Grower's Manual is about financial and business planning. We will look at how to create a business plan and what you need for that, and we get ideas about invoicing, accounting and making sure that you get paid in time.

We will have a look at individual crops, and how well they perform financially. And I hope after reading this chapter you will realise the importance of record keeping, and I will give you some ideas on how to do that.

Record keeping

One of the most important things to do during the growing season is to always keep records of everything that you do, when you do it, and what the results are. Only so can you learn from your mistakes, correct what went wrong this year and expand on what went well next year.

Sowing records

It is good practice to always carry a little notebook with you in which you write down when you sow your crops, which varieties and how many trays or seedlings. Of course you also have to label the seedling trays with the name of the crop, the name of the variety and the date of sowing. I have done this for many years and I have a collection of little notebooks, from which I distil the information for my future cultivation planning.

This has worked well for crops that I only sow once, such as zinnias. I can tell from my little notebook when I sowed the zinnias, how many trays, and when I planted them; and from my sales records (delivery notes or invoices) I can find out when I started harvesting and how many, and for which price I sold them.

However, for crops where I sow several batches, this is not a fail-proof system, as it doesn't allow me to track which batch was successful and which wasn't; or how many stems I harvested

One of my notebooks with weather, sowing and planting records.

Large field label with sowing and planting details.

from a particular batch of sunflowers for example. In order to get that sort of information, I have devised a new system: I write the sowing, planting and harvesting records on big white labels in the ground in each bed, for each batch. Now I am able to record for each batch when it was sown, planted and crucially: when we started harvesting and how much. These labels are often used in scientific field trials, cost about 40p each and can be used for several years – you just need to wipe them clean with white spirit every winter.

Labour records

In order to be able to tell how much you can achieve on your own, or with help of seasonal workers, you need to keep track of how long it takes you to perform the various tasks involved in cut flower production.

It is very useful to make a list for yourself with the various recurrent activities, such as sowing trays, pricking out, transplanting, harvesting, rotavating, etc. With this information you will have a much better idea of how much you can take on – but you only know after a year or two.

Arjen's labour

- filling trays with seedling compost, sowing: 5 trays per hour (126 cells)
- rotavating with the tractor+rotavator: 10 minutes per bed (25 metre)
- transplanting: 4-6 trays per hour (but volunteers often do just 1 tray per hour!)
- picking sweet peas: 20-25 bunches per hour
- bucket washing: 40 buckets per hour
- fertilising beds with chicken manure pellets: 40 beds per hour
- spreading compost in greenhouse with wheelbarrow: 40 sqm per hour
- doing delivery round with 6-8 florists and 80 miles: 3-4 hours

Labour planning

The labour planning is one of the hardest aspects of any type of horticultural endeavour, as so much depends on personal aptitude, skill and ability. Some people can work like a steam engine and achieve an enormous amount of work in a short period of time; others might be much slower but may deliver work of the highest standards.

If you work on your own, you will want to know how much *you* can get done in a certain amount of time. The only way to find out is to *record* what you are doing and how long it takes you. Most of the information in my courses and my hand-outs is based on records I have kept over the years, but even if there *were* books available with this sort of information, it won't necessarily apply to your particular situation - so the most important thing to do during the season is to keep records of how long it takes you to do things. After a year or two you will have very accurate and reliable figures with which you can plan your further growth and possible expansion.

Business planning

Starting your business

Starting a business is exciting and fun, but can also be nerve-wrecking and exhausting. There are so many things to think about, and so many unknowns to work with – although hopefully you will have found a lot of useful data in this book to base your calculations on. Cut flower production is not a business with huge profit margins, so it is important not to get carried away when planning what you want to buy. Instead of buying expensive plants from a nursery try to find out if you can grow them yourself from seeds or cuttings; failing that find a trade nursery where you will be able to buy liners or field-grown plants for a fraction of the price you would pay in a garden centre. Keep the costs down, and try to find as many income streams as possible.

Business structure

Most small growers start their business as a sole trader or a partnership, which means that they are personally liable for all losses and debts. If at some point the business becomes too big and risky for an individual or couple to be liable for, you can turn it into a limited company. It is best to ask for professional advice from for example Business Link or an accountant before setting up a particular business structure.

Capital expenditure

Before you can start growing flowers you will need certain facilities, tools and perhaps machines. The things that last for more than a year, and which you don't use up, are categorised under capital expenditure. The main capital expenditure might well be the land, if you are in a position to buy it. If you lease land it is not called capital expenditure but revenue expenditure, which we will deal with later.

There are several approaches to capital expenditure: some people can afford to buy everything new, and of a high standard. Another approach is the buy everything second-hand, or to buy the cheapest you can get. The third approach, which is what I use at Wealden Flowers, is to buy good quality second-hand tools and machines for the expensive kit, and to buy top quality new tools for everything under 500 pounds.

Here is an example of the kind of capital expenditure you might be looking at for a 1 acre cut flower farm:

for 1 acre of cut flower production			new		second-hand
1 acre of land		£	10,000	£	10,000
rabbit fence incl gate	excl work	£	700	£	700
shed		£	300	£	300
two-wheel tractor with rotavator		£	4,000	£	1,000
small greenhouse	14x8ft excl work	£	1,400	£	200
polytunnel	30x90ft excl work	£	4,500	£	1,000
nurseryman's barrow / long John truck		£	300	£	200
transplant modules	60 modules	£	600	£	300
hand tools	hoes, trowels, etc	£	500	£	250
support netting	250 m incl 250 alu posts	£	800	£	550
buckets	100 buckets	£	200	£	-
mypex ground cover	1000 sqm	£	300	£	300
seed drill	Jang Clean Seeder	£	350	£	350
perennials	1000 plants	£	3,000	£	3,000
total		**£**	**26,950**	**£**	**18,150**

Revenue expenditure

Apart from the initial set-up expenditure, you have recurring costs: things that you need to buy every year and which you usually use up within a year. This is called revenue expenditure and includes things like seeds, transplants, fuel, insurances, etc.

Here is a list of recurring costs which you might incur on a 1 acre cut flower farm:

For 1 acre of cut flower production selling to florists		110 beds of 25 m each		
Seeds			£	300
Transplants	27,000 transplants	£40 per 1000	£	1,080
Tractor hours	40 hours	£10 per hour	£	400
Transport costs (deliveries)	100 miles per week, 26 wks	£0.50 per mile	£	1,300
Packaging (sleeves, elastics)			£	100
Marketing, telephone, website, etc			£	400
Working clothes			£	150
Insurances			£	300
Contingency			£	300
Total			**£**	**4,330**

Revenues

The money you earn when you sell your flowers is called your revenue. Of course you can try to plan that, by looking at your cultivation scheme and put a price per stem against each crop species, as we did in the exercise with the sunflowers. This often has a high margin of error as there are so many unknown factors, especially when you just start growing cut flowers. However, after a year or two, if you have kept good records of production and sales, you will be able to estimate and plan your revenues much more accurately.

In the example above, where we planted 27,000 transplants, a very rough guess might be, if you assume an average return of 70p per plant: 27,000 x 0.70 = £18,900.

Profit

The difference between your expenses and your revenues is your gross profit (or loss...). In the example above you would have made a gross profit of £18,900 - £4,330 = £14,570. From that £14,570 you will need to pay repairs for your investments, as well as allow for depreciation. That means you'll have a net profit of around £12,000 – and that for about 6 months of work: that is not the worst paid job in the world and if you factor in the unlimited joy and sense of pride and achievement as you deliver your flowers to the flower shops you will appreciate the priceless contribution to your own happiness and wellbeing.

Gross margins

You will have the data to decide whether a particular crop is worthwhile or not, and you may decide that there are some crops you shouldn't be growing – simply because you spend too much time on them without any return. But you will also find out which crops don't cost so much time and with which you earn some good money.

With this information you can compile so called "crop gross margins" which show the inputs and the output of each crop in a standardised way. In this way you can compare crops, and choose which crops work for you.

In the appendices you can find the crop gross margins for several crops at Wealden Flowers. You can use the same format to create your own gross margins, based on your own data from the records you have kept throughout the growing season.

You will see from my gross margins that for most crops, labour is the largest cost involved in production. It is helpful to allocate a certain hourly rate for your work, in my case I used £10. If after a few years you are able to hire some help during the growing season, at least you know that you will be able to cover the cost of that, and it won't affect your gross margins too much.

Banking

A business needs its own business bank account – several banks offer free business banking with online banking thrown in. Compare banks online, and find one with a branch nearby.

Paypal is very useful if you sell goods online, for example if you plan to sell flowers through your website. Paypal takes a certain percentage from every payment, comparable to a credit card facility from your bank. On the other hand, Paypal is widely known and used, and it integrates with the invoicing function in Xero (see below).

Accounting

Every business needs to keep track of income and expenditure, and create a profit and loss account at the end of the financial year in order to calculate taxes due. In the olden days accounting would be done in books (ledgers) and was a dull and boring activity. Since the arrival of computers it has become slightly more interesting, and nearly all companies use an accounting software package these days. These computer programmes are often still very cumbersome to work with, and I can't really recommend any one of them.

More recently online accounting packages have appeared on the internet, and some of these can connect with your online business bank account to facilitate easy and quick bank statement reconciliation. At Wealden Flowers we use Xero, which is an absolute pleasure to work with – and which gives us up-to-date information on who has paid their bills, and how the business is doing financially at any point in time. Highly recommended.

VAT

If your turnover is below a certain threshold (in 2012: £77,000 – this changes every year so check with HMRC) you don't have to register for VAT, but there may be good reasons to do so anyway. If you are selling most of your flowers to other businesses (florists, etc) then it is a good idea to register for VAT. When you are registered for VAT, you will get the 20% VAT back from HMRC on everything that you buy for your business. Of course you will have to charge your customers VAT, but if they are a business themselves and registered for VAT, they will be able to reclaim that in turn from HMRC. So for a VAT-registered business your goods are not getting more expensive when you add VAT to your bills, since they will be able to claim back the VAT. Especially when you start your business, and will be buying lots of expensive items such as a tractor, greenhouse or polytunnel, tools and equipment, it is important to make sure you are registered for VAT in order to be able to reclaim the 20% VAT.

If you are unsure, please ask for advice from an accountant or Business Link.

Invoicing and payments

It is common practice to add a delivery note with every consignment you send to a wholesaler or florist. As the supplier you make sure you keep copies of each delivery note. After a set period (one or two weeks) or at the end of the month you gather all the delivery notes and send an invoice to the customer, which they then have to pay within a month or two, depending on your terms and conditions.

Another way of dealing with invoicing is, instead of using delivery notes, to present an invoice along with the goods and get the florist or wholesaler to either pay immediately in cash or to pay the invoice within a month. Even though cash may seem cumbersome, in fact it is a very useful system to get paid cash on delivery, as it maintains the cash flow of your business and if a customer gets in financial trouble and goes bankrupt at least they don't have any outstanding bills with you. Immediate payment reduces the risk to your business significantly. Flower shops normally have a lot of money going through the till, so a cash-on-delivery system shouldn't be any problem for them and it keeps you from losing sleep over unpaid bills.

Terms and Conditions

Every business should have a set of terms and conditions. These stipulate the terms under which you deal with other businesses and consumers, and should safeguard you from unpleasant altercations when things go wrong: if you can't deliver on time, if you can't deliver exactly the varieties or colours the customer has ordered, etc, etc. In the appendices you can find the terms and conditions for Wealden Flowers which you are welcome to copy and use for your own business.

Business tweaking – improving performance

At the end of the growing season you compile all your sales data and create a list of the best- sellers. If you use accounting software, or an online accounting service like Xero, you can quite easily create Excel sheets in which you can sort columns according to sales per item. In the appendices you can find the "sales by item" list for Wealden Flowers over the years 2008-2012. With this information from your own flower garden you can then start tweaking your business: take the worst performers off your cropping list and think about increasing the area of best performers. Of course this only makes sense if you know there is more demand for the best performers – and sometimes you just need to increase the area of the worst performers in order to improve their contribution to the business turnover. However, try to be ruthless and scrap those crops that have a bad record, especially if they haven't improved after several years of trying. Calendula for example is a crop that has now been removed from my growing schedule after several years of wasting my time and growing space.

Helpful organisations

The "Flowers from the Farm" cooperative has been established in 2011 to help small scale cut flower growers with both cultivation but especially the marketing of their flowers. The organisation has developed a logo as well as a website where florists can identify the cut flower growers in their local area. "Flowers from the Farm" are a network of farmers, smallholders and gardeners who have come together to promote locally-grown cut flowers. Some members grow and sell their own flowers directly to the public at farmers' markets or at wedding fairs, at roadside stands or country shows while others are supplying florists or wholesalers. Working together gives the growers strength and allows them to champion the glories of British cut flowers countrywide.

Another useful organisation is the Association of Specialty Cut Flower Growers (ASCFG) in the USA. Even though there are differences in climate between the USA and the UK, many American growers operate in the pacific North-West which has a very similar climate to ours, and a lot of the information on the members-only ASCFG bulletin board is extremely helpful for both beginning as well as experienced growers. The ASCFG publishes a quarterly magazine called the Cut Flower Quarterly, which reports on research, trials and growers' own experiences.

In the UK I have established the "Flower Grower" email group. This is a very active email group through which UK growers communicate with each other, ask and answer questions and report on which crops and techniques work for them and which don't. You can subscribe for free through the "Wealden Flowers" website (go to "Courses") or through the "Flowers from the Farm" website.

Appendices

Appendix 1: Suppliers for cut flower growers

Roses

Kordes Rosen

www.kordes-rosen.com

Rosen Tantau

http://www.rosen-tantau.com

Flower bulbs (tulips, gladioli, dahlias, anemones, etc)

Verberghe

www.verberghe.nl

Dix Export

www.dixexport.com

Hostas, peonies and irises

Heemskerk

www.heemskerkplants.com

Dahlias

Withypitts Nursery, Turner's Hill

http://www.withypitts-dahlias.co.uk/index.html

Shrubs for cutting

Hendriksen Stekbedrijf

This is the most economical option to obtain shrub material. This company sells unrooted cuttings, which you have to root yourself. Check them first before you check the rest.

http://www.djhendriksen.nl/

Kolster
Specialist breeder for shrubs for cutting. Good hypericums.
www.kolster.nl

Danziger Flower Farm
Isreali breeder of shrubs and perennials for cutting. Nice hypericums, and a new ivory coloured solidago.
www.danziger.il

-representative in the UK: Parigo, www.parigo.co.uk

Bartels Stek
Good varieties of perennials and shrubs.
http://www.bartelsstek.nl/

The Northern Liner Company
Range of landscape shrubs, some suitable for cutting.
www.northernliners.co.uk

Lilacs

Piccoplant
www.piccoplant.de

Micropropagation Services (EM) Ltd
http://micropropagation-services.co.uk/

Seeds

Geoseed
I have used Geoseed for several years now and they are the least expensive company offering the widest range.
www.geoseed.com

Moles Seeds
Moles was my main supplier of annual seeds for several years.
www.molesseeds.co.uk

Kings Seeds
What I can't get from Moles, I buy from Kings.
www.kingsseeds.com

Jelitto Seeds
German breeders of perennials with online order system. Good for delphinium, asparagus, eryngium and many other perennials.
www.jelitto.com

Sakata
www.sakata-eu.com

Benary
German breeder, they have the best zinnias and do good asters too. Order through Moles.
www.benary.com

Tamar Organics
The best company for organic seeds in the UK. Unfortunately they don't have many specialist cut flower varieties, but the sunflowers and ornamental basil from Genesis Seeds are good.
www.tamarorganicspro.co.uk

Genesis Seeds
The only breeder for organic cut flower varieties. Choose varieties on their website, then call Tamar Organics to order.
http://www.genesisseeds.com/

PanAmerican Seeds
Breeders of stocks and antirrhinum (snapdragon) especially. Good cultural descriptions on their website – you can order their seeds through Moles or Fred Gloeckner.
http://www.panamseed.com/

Fred Gloeckner Seeds, USA
Excellent source of many useful varieties, online order system. Best source for celosia and sunflowers (which they sell untreated – hard to come by).
http://www.fredgloeckner.com/

Dowdeswell Delphiniums
Probably the best delphinium breeder in the world – you can get his seeds directly off his website or through Jelitto. Jelitto sells a much cheaper F2 version of his New MIllenium Hybrids – which is probably just as good, even if it has a bit more variation.
http://www.delphinium.co.nz/

Baker Seeds
Source for ornamental gourd varieties.
www.rareseeds.com

Kieft

www.kieft-pro-seeds-com

B&T World Seeds

Rare and unusual seeds can be obtained from B&T, but they're not cheap. Try all others first.
www.b-and-t-world-seeds.com

Sweet pea seeds

Laughing Owl

Laughing Owl Sweet Pea Seeds are the specialist breeder for commercial cut flower production.
www.lathyrus-seed.com

Matthewman's Sweet Peas

http://www.sweetpeasonline.co.uk/

Roger Parsons Sweet Peas

I have had some excellent sweet pea varieties from Roger Parsons, especially the Japanese winter sweet pea varieties.
http://www.rpsweetpeas.co.uk/index.htm

National Sweet Pea Society

http://www.sweetpeas.org.uk/

Equipment

Tuinbouwmarktplaats (only in Dutch)

Excellent website where the Dutch growers sell their surplus equipment and planting material.
www.tuinbouwmarktplaats.nl

Duijndam Machines

All sorts of used machinery for horticultural enterprises.
www.duijndam.nl

Affordable Tractors

Direct import of low-hour used small tractors from Japan.
www.affordabletractors.co.uk

Pasquali Tractors

Good quality, reasonably priced Italian equipment
http://www.pasqualitractors.co.uk/

The Market Garden Supply Company
Jang seed drills, wheel hoes:
http://themarketgardener.co.uk/

Lows of Dundee
Fleece, mulch plastic, cover plastic, plastic pots:
http://www.lowsofdundee.co.uk/

Harrod's Horticultural
Supplies hand-forged stainless steel Sneeboer hand tools – my favourite tools!
www.harrodhorticultural.com

Two West's and Elliott
Complete mist propagator units
www.twowests.co.uk

Simply Control
Mist controllers, nozzles, etc for DIY mist propagation systems
www.simplycontrol.com

Haygrove Tunnels
Spanish tunnels
www.haygrove.co.uk

Sundries

Horticultural Supplies
organic potting soil (Klassmann), vermiculite, 6x organic chicken manure pellets
www.horticulturalsupplies.co.uk

Rootgrow (Mycorrhizal fungi)
www.rootgrow.co.uk

Plant Health Care
organic liquid fertiliser, mycorrhizae, etc
www.planthealthcare.co.uk

Chrysal Products:
Dejex Supplies Ltd
www.dejex.co.uk

Pagter
Procona flower buckets for transport
www.pagter.com

Plug trays:

Containerwise Materials Handling Ltd
www.containerwise.co.uk

Beekenkamp Verpakkingen
http://verpakkingen.beekenkamp.nl/

Promens BV
+31 316 586100
paul.de.reus@promens.com

Waterproof trousers:

I recommend Flexothane bib and brace trousers, available from:
www.bestworkwear.co.uk

Dungaree style working trousers with knee pockets:

I recommend Carhartt, available from (search for Carhartt R01):
http://www.performanceworkclothing.co.uk

Irrigation: drip tape, Techline etc:

Fargro
http://www.fargro.co.uk/

Access Irrigation
http://www.access-irrigation.co.uk/

Appendix 2: Building instructions for harvesting trolleys

The harvest trolleys are very useful when harvesting flowers from beds. The trolleys are very narrow and fit neatly between the flower beds.

Needed:

- 4 pieces of strip metal (5mm thick) 590mm x 25mm
- 4 pieces of strip metal (5mm thick) 500mm x 25mm
- 4 pieces of strip metal (5mm thick) 300mm x 25mm
- 2 pieces of strip metal (5mm thick) 510mm x 25mm, bent to create a U shaped bracket for the wheels with 220mm legs and 60mm space between the legs (check with wheels!)
- 1 piece of steel tube (16mm diameter) 590mm, bent to create a U shaped bracket with 140mm legs and 300mm space between the legs – ends hammered flat
- 1 piece of steel tube (16mm diameter) 810mm, bent to create a U shaped bracket with 250mm legs and 300mm space between the legs – ends hammered flat
- 2 pieces of steel tube (16mm diameter) 780mm, bent to create V shaped legs, see drawing
- 2 wheels 12.5" (these might be the hardest to find – after a long search on the internet I found the following supplier: Wright Buyers, C/O Arrows corporation Ltd, Unit 3D Bergen Close, Tyne Tunnel Trading Estate, Tyne and Wear NE29 7TA, Phone: 0191 2966966, Email: service@wrightbuyers.co.uk – they also sell these on eBay "12.5 x 2.50 REPLACEMENT SACK TRUCK TROLLEY WHEELBARROW WHEEL")
- 2 steel rods (6mm diameter) 750mm length, 50mm at each end bent at a 90 degree angle
- a piece of synthetic cloth or fleece 580mm x 1400mm, with both short ends stitched to create a 50mm hem through which the steel rods fit so as to create a "hammock" for the flowers. The sheet after hemming measures 580mm x 1300mm.

Harvest trolley with fleece "hammock"

The narrow footprint of the harvest trolley allows easy access between the flower beds

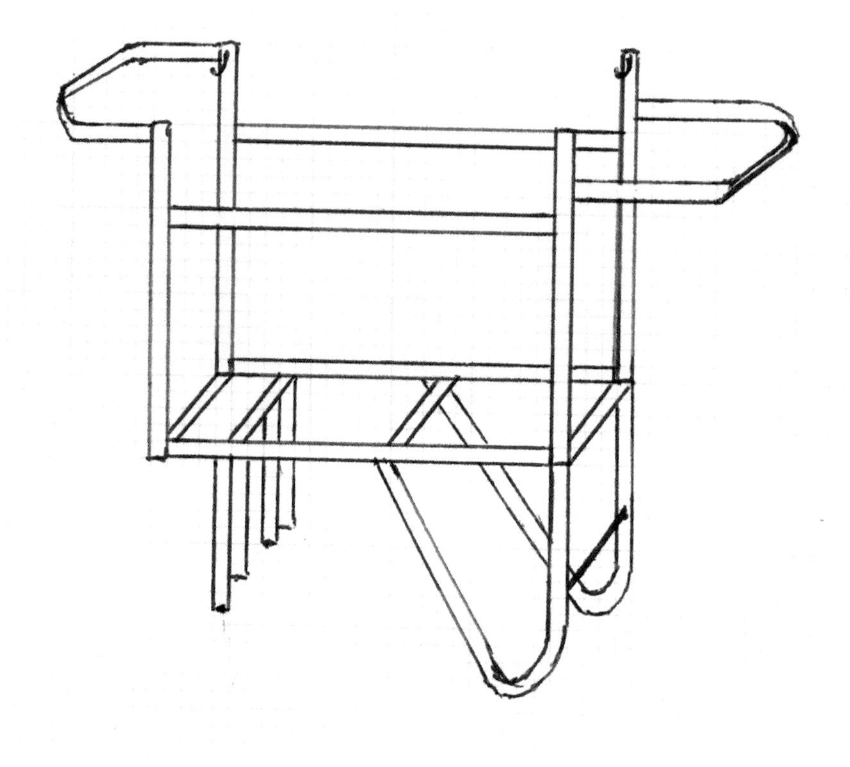

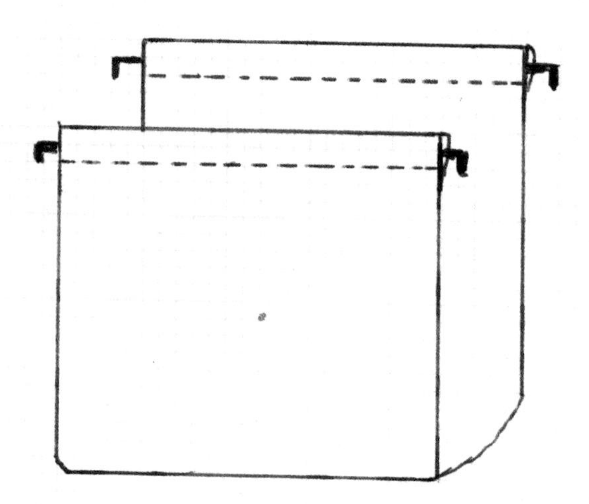

Three-dimensional view of the harvest trolley construction and the fleece "hammock".

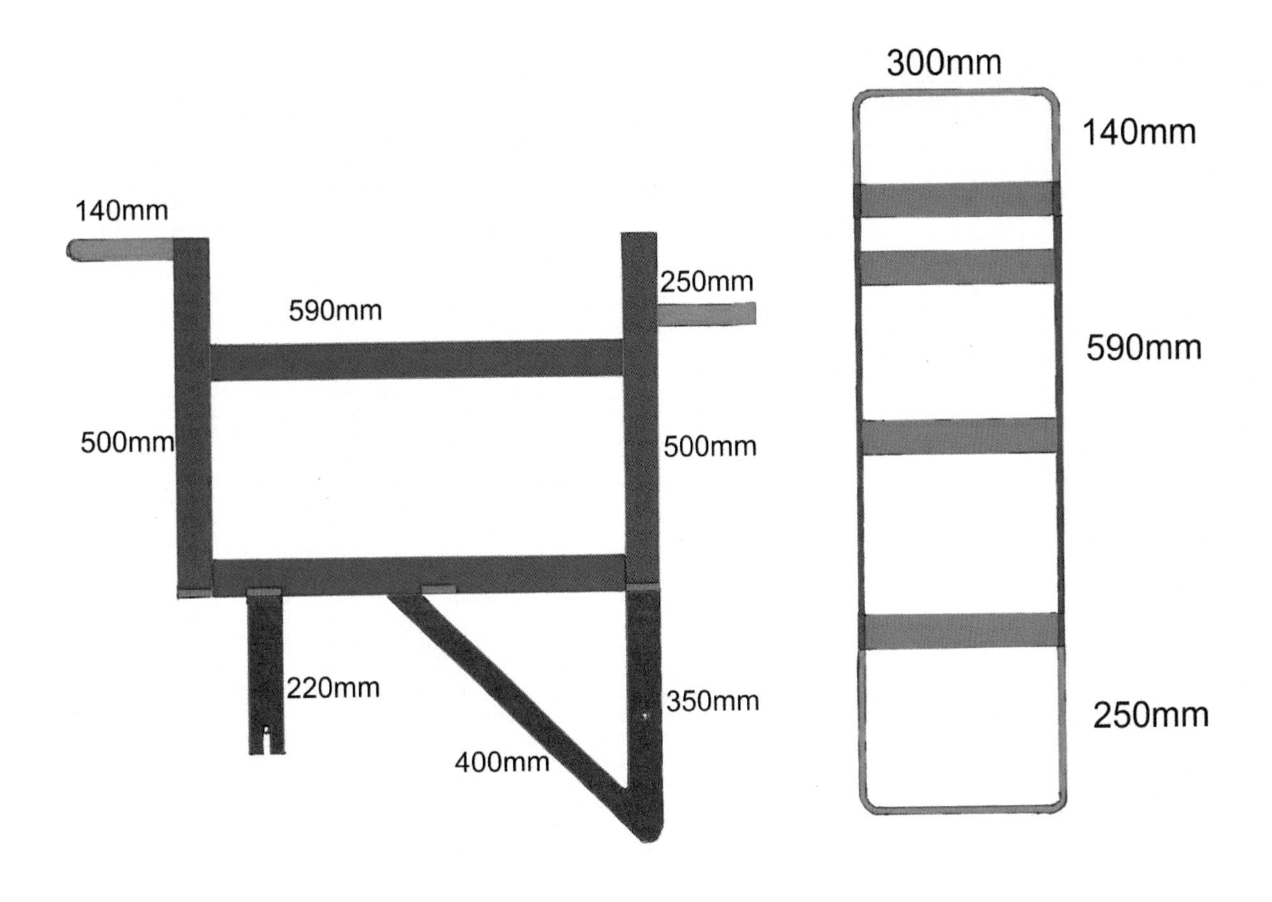

Side view of the harvest trolley

Top view of the harvest trolley

Appendix 3: Toilet cistern bucket filler

Filling buckets with a hose and spray gun is a time consuming task, and more so if the water pressure is relatively low. On top of that it is not easy to estimate how many litres of water you have put in a bucket – especially if you use buckets of various shapes and sizes.

The toilet cistern bucket filler solves both problems: with a press on the button you fill a bucket with an exact amount of water in a very short space of time. This is how it works: you attach an ordinary toilet cistern to the wall of your shed, and connect it up to the mains. On the outlet you attach a simple pipe which conducts the water into the bucket you position underneath the cistern.

Most modern toilet cisterns have an internal control screw which you can find when you open the lid on the cistern. With this screw you can adjust the amount of water that is being flushed down the loo every time you press the button. You can adjust this to your needs, for example 2 or 3 litres of water for each flower bucket. If you have an older model of toilet cistern without the adjustment screw you will have to put some clean bricks in the cistern to reduce the amount of water per flush (usually 10 litres).

You can improve the system by installing two or three toilet cisterns, for example a one-and-a-half litre cistern for sweet peas (this is the amount we use when we make silver thiosulphate solutions), and a couple of cisterns with 3 litres for the standard CVBn solution, so you always have enough capacity when you are harvesting.

(Above): Inside the cistern, with the blue adjustment screw on the left hand side.

Appendix 4: Crop scheduling

Crop Schedule poster

© Arjen Huese 2012

s sowing | growing | p transplanting | h harvesting

transplant growing | pot potting up in 7cm pots | h(2) harvest only in the second year or from second year onwards

			early	late	early	late	early	late	early	late	early	late	early	late	early	late	early	late	early	late	early	late	early	late	early	late
			jan	jan	feb	feb	march	march	april	april	may	may	june	june	july	july	aug	aug	sept	sept	oct	oct	nov	nov	dec	dec
Achillea		p	s					p							h	h	h	h								
Achillea ptarmica	The Pearl	p	s					p								h	h	h								
Agastache		a			s				p	p							h	h	h							
Alcea		p																								
Alchemilla		p								s		p	h(2)	h(2)												
Allium		a								h	h										p	p				
Amaranthus	early	a							s		p				h	h										
Amaranthus	late	a											s	p			h	h	h							
Ammi	early	a					s			p				h	h	h										
Ammi	mid	a								s		p			h	h	h									
Ammi	late	a														h	h	h	h	h						
Antirrhinum	overwintering cold greenhouse	a	p									h	h								s					
Antirrhinum Potomac	early	a	s					p					h	h												
Antirrhinum Rocket	early	a	s					p						h	h											
Antirrhinum Rocket	mid	a				s			p							h	h									
Antirrhinum Rocket	mid-late	a						s			p							h	h							
Antirrhinum Rocket	late	a								s			p						h	h	h					
Artichoke		p			s				p									h	h	h						
Asparagus		p						s				p/h(2)	h(2)	h(2)	h(2)	h(2)										
Bupleurum	early	a						s	s		p				h	h	h									
Bupleurum	mid	a									s		p					h	h							
Bupleurum	late	a											s		p					h	h					
Calendula	early	a							s		p			h	h											
Calendula	mid	a									s		p			h	h									
Calendula	late	a											s		p			h	h	h						
Callistephus		a							s		p						h	h	h							
Campanula		p								s	s		p/h(2)	h(2)												
Canterbury Bells		b								s	s		p/h(2)	h(2)												
Clary sage	early	a							s		p				h	h	h									
Clary sage	late	a									s		p					h	h	h						
Celosia	greenhouse	a							s				p					h	h	h						
Cornflower	early	a							s	p				h	h											
Cornflower	mid	a									s	p				h	h									
Cornflower	late	a												s	p			h	h	h						
Cosmos		a					s	s				p				h	h	h								
Dahlia	plant pre-sprouted tubers	a								p	p			h	h	h	h	h	h	h						
Delphinium		p		s				pot		p			h	h	h											
Digitalis	FYF available	p		s				p				h/h(2)	h/h(2)													
Dill	early	a						s		p				h	h	h										
Dill	mid	a								s		p					h	h								
Dill	late	a										s		p					h	h						

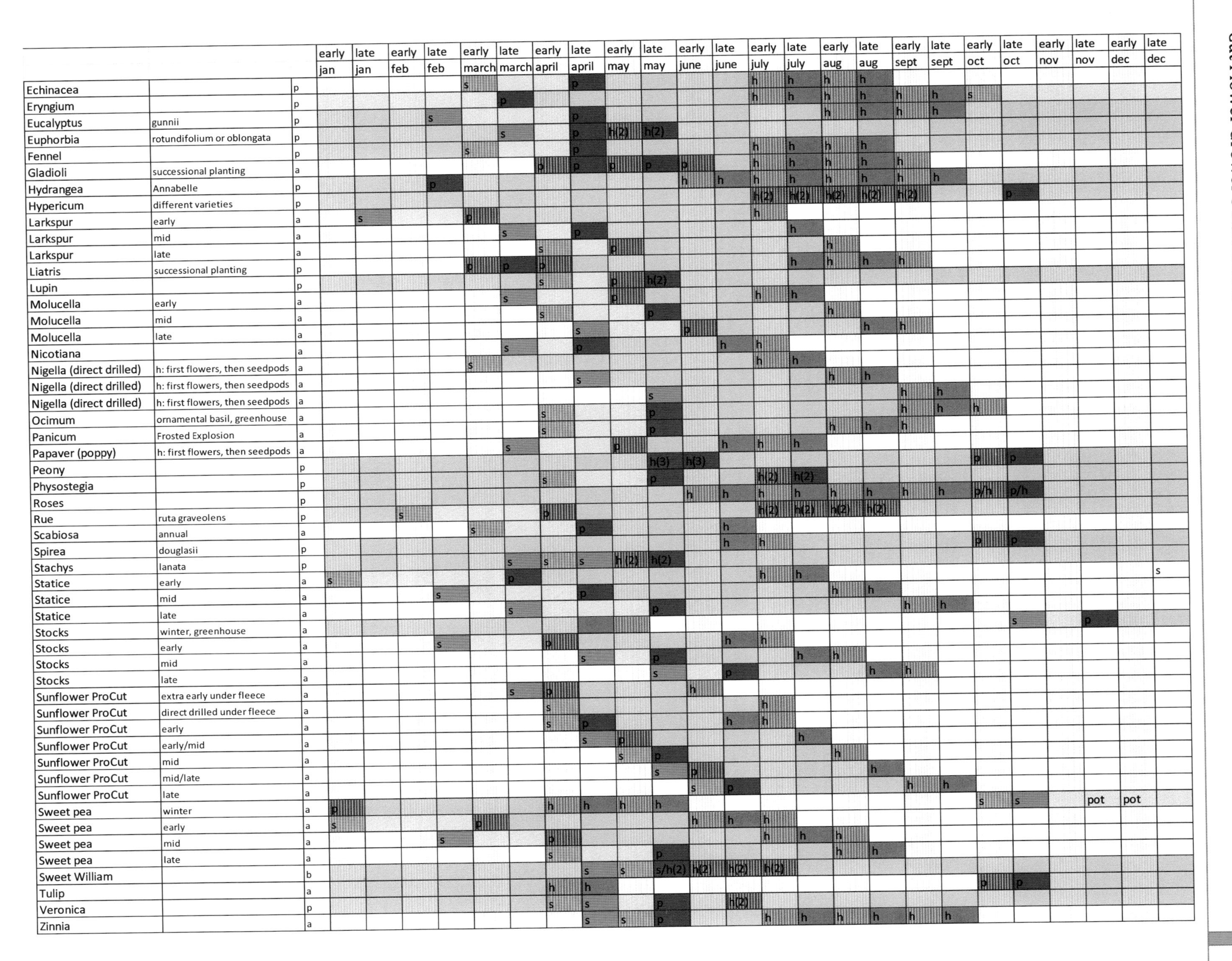

			early	late	early	late	early	late	early	late	early	late	early	late	early	late	early	late	early	late	early	late	early	late	early	late
			jan	jan	feb	feb	march	march	april	april	may	may	june	june	july	july	aug	aug	sept	sept	oct	oct	nov	nov	dec	dec
Echinacea		p					s			p					h	h	h	h								
Eryngium		p						p							h	h	h	h	h	h	s					
Eucalyptus	gunnii	p				s				p							h	h	h	h						
Euphorbia	rotundifolium or oblongata	p						s		p	h(2)	h(2)														
Fennel		p					s			p					h	h	h	h								
Gladioli	successional planting	a							p	p	p	p	p		h	h	h	h	h							
Hydrangea	Annabelle	p				p							h	h	h	h	h	h	h	h						
Hypericum	different varieties	p													h(2)	h(2)	h(2)	h(2)	h(2)			p				
Larkspur	early	a		s			p								h											
Larkspur	mid	a						s		p						h										
Larkspur	late	a							s		p						h									
Liatris	successional planting	p					p	p	p							h	h	h	h							
Lupin		p							s		p	h(2)														
Molucella	early	a						s			p				h	h										
Molucella	mid	a							s			p					h									
Molucella	late	a								s			p					h	h							
Nicotiana		a						s		p				h	h											
Nigella (direct drilled)	h: first flowers, then seedpods	a					s								h	h										
Nigella (direct drilled)	h: first flowers, then seedpods	a								s							h	h								
Nigella (direct drilled)	h: first flowers, then seedpods	a										s							h	h						
Ocimum	ornamental basil, greenhouse	a							s			p							h	h	h					
Panicum	Frosted Explosion	a							s			p					h	h	h							
Papaver (poppy)	h: first flowers, then seedpods	a						s			p			h	h	h										
Peony		p										h(3)	h(3)								p	p				
Physostegia		p							s			p			h(2)	h(2)										
Roses		p											h	h	h	h	h	h	h	h	p/h	p/h				
Rue	ruta graveolens	p			s				p						h(2)	h(2)	h(2)	h(2)								
Scabiosa	annual	a					s			p				h												
Spirea	douglasii	p												h	h						p	p				
Stachys	lanata	p						s	s	s	h(2)	h(2)														
Statice	early	a	s					p							h	h										s
Statice	mid	a				s				p							h	h								
Statice	late	a						s				p							h	h						
Stocks	winter, greenhouse	a																				s		p		
Stocks	early	a				s			p					h	h											
Stocks	mid	a								s		p				h	h									
Stocks	late	a										s		p				h	h							
Sunflower ProCut	extra early under fleece	a						s	p				h													
Sunflower ProCut	direct drilled under fleece	a							s						h											
Sunflower ProCut	early	a							s	p				h	h											
Sunflower ProCut	early/mid	a								s	p					h										
Sunflower ProCut	mid	a									s	p					h									
Sunflower ProCut	mid/late	a										s	p					h								
Sunflower ProCut	late	a											s	p					h	h						
Sweet pea	winter	a	p						h	h	h	h									s	s		pot	pot	
Sweet pea	early	a	s				p						h	h	h											
Sweet pea	mid	a				s			p						h	h	h									
Sweet pea	late	a							s			p					h	h								
Sweet William		b								s	s	s/h(2)	h(2)	h(2)	h(2)						p	p				
Tulip		a							h	h																
Veronica		p							s	s		p		h(2)												
Zinnia		a								s	s	p			h	h	h	h	h	h						

Appendix 5: Optimum harvesting stage

Acacia spp.	half of the florets open
Achillea filipendulina	fully open flowers
Aconitum napellus	half of the florets open
Agapanthus umbellatus	quarter of the florets open
Allium spp.	quarter to third of the florets open
Alstroemeria hybrids	4-5 florets open
Althea rosea	third of the florets open
Amaranthus	half of the florets open
Ammi majus, A. visnaga	fully open flowers
Anemone coronaria	buds beginning to open
Anthurium spp.	spadix almost fully developed
Antirrhinum majus	up to third of the florets open
Aquilegia hybrids	half of the florets open
Astilbe hybrids	half of the florets open
Bellis perennis	fully open flowers
Bouvardia hybrids	flowers beginning to open
Bupleurum griffithii	flowers fully open
Calendula officinalis	fully open flowers
Callistephus chinensis	fully open flowers
Camellia japonica	fully open flowers
Campanula spp.	half of the florets open
Cattleya spp.	3-4 days after opening
Celosia argentea	half of the florets open
Centaurea spp.	flowers beginning to open
Cheiranthus cheirii	half of the florets open
Chrysanthemum spp.	fully open flowers
Chrysanthemum morifolium	
Standard cultivars	outer petals fully elongated
Spray cultivars	
Singles	open but before the anthers start shedding pollen
Anemones	open but before disk flowers start to elongate
Pompons and decorative	centre of the oldest flower fully open
Clarkia elegans	half of the florets open
Consolida ambigua	2-5 florets open
Convallaria majalis	half of the florets open
Coreopsis grandiflora	fully open flowers
Crocosmia crocosmiflora	half of the florets open
Cyclamen persicum	fully open flowers
Dahlia variabilis	fully open flowers
Delphinium spp.	half of the florets open
Dianthus barbatus	half of the florets open
Dianthus caryophyllus	
Standard cultivars	half-open flowers
Spray cultivars	2 fully open flowers

Digitalis purpurea	half of the florets open
Doronicum caucasicum	almost open flowers
Echinops ritro	half-open flowers
Eremurus robustus	half of the florets open
Erica spp.	half of the florets open
Erigeron hybrids	fully open flowers
Eryngium spp.	fully open flowers, panicles need to be firmed up, don't harvest too green as this will result in drooping
Euphorbia fulgens	showing enough colour to be fully mature
Euphorbia pulcherrima	showing enough colour to be fully mature
Eustoma russellianum	5-6 open flowers
Freesia hybrids	first bud beginning to open
Fritillaria imperialis	half-open flowers
Gaillardia	fully open flowers
Gardenia jasminoides	almost fully open flowers
Gerbera jamesonii	outer ring of flowers showing pollen
Gladiolus cultivars	1-5 buds showing colour
Gloriosa superba	almost fully open flowers
Gypsophila spp.	flowers open but not overly mature
Helianthus annuus	flowers just showing colour, half open
Heliopsis helianthoides	fully open flowers
Helleborus niger	wait until the seedpods are starting to form
Hemerocallis spp.	half-open flowers
Hippeastrum hybrids	coloured buds
Hydrangea arborescens "Annabelle"	fully open flowers, may be slightly green
Hypericum spp.	fully coloured berries
Iris spp.	coloured buds
Ixia spp.	coloured buds
Kalanchoe hybrids	half of the florets open
Kniphofia uvaria	almost all florets showing colour
Lathyrus odoratus	half of the florets open
Leontopodium alpinum	fully open flowers
Liatris spicata	half of the florets open
Lilium spp.	coloured buds
Limonium spp.	almost fully open flowers
Lupinus mutabilis	half of the florets open
Matthiola incana	half of the florets open
Molucella laevis	harvest after little white flowers have fallen off
Monarda didyma	almost open flowers
Muscari botryoides	half of the florets open
Myosotis silvatica	half of the florets open
Narcissus spp.	"goose neck" stage
Nepeta faassenii	half of the florets open
Nerine bowdenii	oldest buds almost open
Nigella damascena	just open flowers (stamens still together) or wait for seedpods

Ornithogalum spp.	coloured buds
Paeonia spp.	soft coloured buds, "marshmallow stage"
Papaver spp.	coloured buds or wait for seedpods
Phlox paniculata	half of the florets open
Physostegia virginiana	half of the florets open
Polianthes tuberosa	majority of florets open
Primula spp.	half of the florets open
Ranunculus asiaticus	buds beginning to open
Reseda odorata	half of the florets open
Rosa hybrids	
Red and pink cultivars	first 2 petals beginning to unfold, calyx reflexed below a horizontal position
Yellow cultivars	slightly earlier than red and pink
White cultivars	slightly later than red and pink
Rudbeckia spp.	fully open flowers
Salvia horminum	bracts fully coloured
Scabiosa spp.	half-open flowers
Scilla sibirica	half-open flowers
Sedum spp.	fully open flowers
Solidago spp.	half of the florets open
Spirea douglasii	just before florets open
Stachys byzantina	before the actual flowers appear
Stephanotis floribunda	open flowers
Tagetes erecta	fully open flowers
Thalictrum aguilegifolium	half of the florets open
Trollius spp.	half-open flowers
Tulipa spp.	half-coloured buds
Veronica spp.	half of the florets open
Viburnum opulus roseum	green/white flowers
Viola odorata	almost open flowers
Viola x wittrockiana	almost open flowers
Zantedeschia spp.	just before the spathe begins to turn downward
Zinnia elegans	fully open flowers

Appendix 6: Estimated average yield per plant

	Estimated average yield / plant			
	1st year	2nd year	3rd year	Comments:
Achillea	15	40	35	
Achillea ptarmica	15	25		
Agastache	1			
Alcea	1			
Alchemilla	?	5		
Allium	1			
Amaranthus	1			
Ammi	5			
Antirrhinum	3			
Artichoke	1			
Artichoke (pinched)	3			
Asparagus	1	5	8	
Bupleurum	4			
Calendula	1			
Callistephus	1			
Campanula	0	1	?	
Canterbury Bells	0	1		
Clary sage	3			often sold by bundle not by stem count
Celosia	1			
Cornflower	3			often sold by bundle not by stem count
Cosmos	4			
Dahlia	3			
Delphinium	1	?	?	
Digitalis	1	?	?	
Dill	2			
Echinacea	1	4	6	
Eryngium	3	6	9	
Eucalyptus	1	?	?	
Euphorbia oblongata	0	5	?	first year stems too short
Fennel	1	?	?	
Gladioli	1			
Hydrangea "Annabelle"	2	5	10	
Hypericum	0	6	8	first year stems too short
Larkspur	1			
Liatris	3	8	15	
Lupin	0	3	?	
Molucella	1			
Nicotiana	1			
Nigella (direct drilled)	1			often sold by bundle not by stem count
Ocimum	2			
Panicum	8			
Papaver (poppy)	3			
Peony	0	0	5-10	
Physostegia	0	5	?	
Roses	1	2	2	my yields are not representative - but real
Rue	0	?	?	
Scabiosa	?	13	?	
Spirea douglasii	0	?	?	so far only harvested from established shrubs
Stachys	0	2	?	
Statice	12			
Stocks	1			
Sunflower ProCut	1			
Sunflower ProCut (pinched)	3			
Sweet pea	10			
Sweet William	5			
Tulip	1			
Veronica	50	80	30	
Zinnia	3			

Appendix 7: Terms and Conditions

These are the terms and conditions as used by my business, Wealden Flowers. You are welcome to copy them and use them, but I cannot accept any liability for any damage which may result from your use of these terms and conditions. They are only printed here as an example of business terms and conditions.

Terms and Conditions

A&M Huese, t/a Wealden Flowers
Emerson College, Hartfield Road
Forest Row, East Sussex, RH18 5JX

These Conditions shall be deemed to be incorporated into every contract entered into by A&M Huese trading as Wealden Flowers ("the Company") to sell goods and shall, notwithstanding any statement to the contrary contained in any communications by the person, firm or company with whom any contract to sell goods is made by the Company ("the Customer"), prevail over any conflicting or inconsistent Terms and Conditions contained in any order, telex, letter, or form of contract sent by the Customer to the Company or any other communication between the Customer and the Company whatsoever and whatever their respective dates unless or to the extent that any variation of these Conditions shall be expressly agreed in writing and signed by one of the Company's directors.

1. Price

1.1 The price quoted excludes VAT (unless otherwise stated.) VAT will be charged at the rate applying at the time of delivery.

1.2 The price quoted excludes delivery (unless otherwise stated).

1.3 Unless otherwise stated, the price quoted is an illustrative estimate only and the price charged will be our price current at the time of delivery.

1.4 Rates of tax and duties on the goods will be those applying at the time of delivery.

1.5 At any time before delivery we may adjust the price to reflect any increase in our costs of supplying the goods.

2. Delivery

2.1 All delivery times quoted are estimates only. Time shall not be the essence for delivery.

2.2 If we fail to deliver within a reasonable time, you may (by informing us in writing) cancel the order however:

2.2.1 you may not cancel if we receive your notice after the goods have been dispatched: and

2.2.2 if you cancel the order you can have no further claim against us under that contract.

2.3 If you accept delivery of the goods after the estimated delivery time, it will be on the basis that you have no claim against us for delay (including indirect or consequential loss, or increase in the price of the goods).

2.4 We may deliver goods in instalments. Each instalment is treated as a separate contract.

3. Delivery and Safety

3.1 We may decline to deliver if:

3.1.1 we believe that it would be unsafe, unlawful or unreasonably difficult to do so; or

3.1.2 the premises (or the access to them) are unsuitable for our vehicle.

4. Risk

4.1 The goods are at your risk from the time of delivery.

4.2 Delivery takes place either:

4.2.1 at our premises (if you are collecting them or arranging carriage); or

4.2.2 at your premises (if we are arranging carriage).

4.3 You must inspect the goods on delivery. Any claims must be notified to us within 48 hours of delivery and confirm your claim in writing within 7 days.

You must give us (and any carrier) a fair chance to inspect the damaged goods.

4.4 If by prior agreement, we deliver the goods outside your normal business hours, you must inspect the goods as soon after delivery as possible. If you do not notify us of any damaged or undelivered goods within 48 hours of delivery, we may treat you as having accepted that the goods were delivered in the quantities stated on the delivery note and at the time recorded by our driver.

5. Payment terms

5.1 You are to pay us in cash or otherwise in cleared funds immediately upon delivery or collection for all goods, unless you have an approved credit account.

5.2 If you have an approved credit account, payment is due no later than 14 days after the date of our invoice unless otherwise agreed in writing.

5.3 If you fail to pay us in full on the due date:

5.3.1 we may suspend or cancel future deliveries:

5.3.2 you must pay us interest at the rate set under s.6 of the Late Payment of Commercial Debts (Interest) Act 1998:-

(a) calculated (on a daily basis) from the date of our invoice until payment;

(b) compounded on the first day of each month; and

(c) before and after any judgment (unless a court orders otherwise);

5.3.3 we may claim fixed sum compensation from you under s.5A of that Act to cover our credit control overhead costs; and

5.3.4 we may recover (under clause 5.7) the cost of taking legal action to make you pay.

5.4 If you have an approved credit account, we may withdraw it or reduce your credit limit or bring forward your due date for payment. We may do any of those at any time without notice.

5.5 You do not have the right to offset any money you may claim from us against anything you may owe us.

5.6 While you owe money to us, we have a lien on any of your property in our possession.

5.7 You are to indemnify us in full and hold us harmless from all expenses and liabilities we may incur (directly or indirectly including financing costs and including legal costs in a full indemnity basis) following any breach by you of any of your obligations under these terms

6. Title

6.1 Under these Conditions, until you pay all debts you may owe us:

6.1.1 all goods supplied by us remain our property;

6.1.2 you must store them so that they are clearly identifiable as our property;

6.1.3 you must insure them (against the risks for which a prudent owner would insure them) and hold the policy on trust for us:

6.1.4 you may use those goods and sell them in the ordinary course of your business, but not if:

(a) we revoke that right (by informing you in writing); or

(b) you become insolvent.

6.2 You must inform us (in writing) immediately if you become insolvent.

6.3 If your right to use and sell the goods ends you must allow us to remove the goods.

6.4 We have your permission to enter any premises where the goods may be stored:

6.4.1 at any time, to inspect them; and

6.4.2 after your right to use and sell them has ended, to remove them, using reasonable force if necessary.

6.5 Despite our retention of title to the goods we have the right to take legal proceedings to recover the price of goods supplied should you not pay us by the due date.

6.6 You are not our agent. You have no authority to make any contract on our behalf or in our name.

7. Disclaimer and Limitation of Liability

7.1 Whilst we agree to use our reasonable endeavours to ensure that the Company web site and correspondence are fully operational and error-free, we cannot guarantee this and therefore accept no responsibility for any defects and/or interruption of the Company site and/or the Company service and shall be released from our obligations under these Terms and Conditions in the event of any cause beyond our reasonable control which renders the provision of the Company site and/or the Company service impossible or impractical.

7.2 The information on this web site may contain technical inaccuracies or typographical errors. Information may be changed or updated without notice by the Company and the Company may also make improvements and/or changes to this information at any time without notice.

7.3 All goods and products shown on this web site are representations only of the designs that will be delivered by the Company.

7.4 As flower growers and in order to achieve maximum longevity for our customers fresh flowers are dispatched in the condition in which they are harvested which may be in "bud" or "unopened" condition; customers who require flowers to be in an "open" condition should take account of prevailing temperatures and place their orders accordingly as we cannot guarantee when the flowers will be in the condition required for use.

7.5 All goods and products shown on this website and in our email communication are representations of the goods and designs that will be delivered by the Company on a bespoke basis to comply with your particular order and as such we cannot guarantee that your goods or product will look exactly like the design shown on the website or in our email communication including the pictures shown on this site which are for guidance only and in particular no liability is accepted for any variation in hue or colour of goods or products to be delivered.

7.6 We accept liability for death or personal injury arising from our negligence.

7.7 Subject to clause 7.6, our liability in contract, tort (including negligence and breach of statutory duty) or otherwise arising by reason of or in connection with your order with us shall be limited to the price you have paid for the Company products.

7.8 Subject to clauses 7.6 we exclude all liability for any claims, losses, demands and damages, including without limitation, any costs, loss of profits, loss of contracts or business opportunity, loss of data and any other consequential, incidental, special or punitive damages, even if we have been advised of the possibility of such damages, arising directly or indirectly out of or in any way connected with your use or inability to access the Company site and/or the Company service, whether arising in contract, tort (including negligence), under statute or otherwise PROVIDED THAT nothing contained in these Terms and Conditions affects or will affect your or the recipient's statutory rights in relation to the quality, fitness or description of the Company products supplied.

7.9 Subject to clauses 7.6 above, we shall not be liable for any delay or inability to perform our obligations to you if such delay is due to any cause whatsoever beyond our reasonable control.

8. Cancellation

8.1 If the order is cancelled (for any reason) you are then to pay us for all stock (finished or unfinished) that we may then hold (or to which we are committed) for the order.

8.2 We may suspend or cancel the order, by written notice if:

8.2.1 you fail to pay us any money when due (under the order or otherwise)

8.2.2 you become insolvent or the Company believes on reasonable grounds that any payment will not be met by the Customer when due;

8.2.3 you fail to honour your obligations under these terms.

8.3 You may not cancel the order unless we agree in writing (and clauses 2.2.2 and 8.1 then apply)

9. Waiver and variations

9.1 Any waiver or variation of these terms is binding in honour only unless:

9.1.1 made (or recorded) in writing;

9.1.2 signed on behalf of each party; and

9.1.3 expressly stating an intention to vary these terms.

9.2 All orders that you place with us will be on these terms (or any that we may issue to replace them). By placing an order with us, you are expressly waiving any printed terms you may have to extent that they are inconsistent with our terms.

10. Force majeure

10.1 The Company shall not be liable for any default due to any circumstance beyond the reasonable control of the Company including, but not limited to, Acts of God, war, civil unrest, riot, strike, lock-out, acts of civil or military authorities, fire, flood, earthquake or shortage of supply.

11. General

11.1 English law is applicable to any contract made under these terms. The English and Welsh courts have non-exclusive jurisdiction.

11.2 In these Conditions, references to the masculine include the feminine and the neuter and to the singular include the plural and vice versa as the context admits or requires.

11.3 Any reference in these Conditions to any provisions of a statute shall be construed as a reference to that provision as amended, re-enacted or extended at the relevant time.

11.4 The headings in these Conditions are for convenience only and shall not affect their interpretation.

11.5 If you are any more than one persons, each of you has joint and several obligations under these terms.

11.6 If any of these terms are unenforceable as drafted:

11.6.1 it will not affect the enforceability of any other of these terms; and

11.6.2 if it would be enforceable if amended, it will be treated as so amended.

11.7 We may treat you as insolvent if:

11.7.1 you are unable to pay your debts as they fall due; or

11.7.2 you (or any item of your property) become the subject of:

(a) any formal insolvency procedure (examples of which include receivership, liquidation, administration, voluntary arrangements (including a moratorium) or bankruptcy);

(b) any application or proposal for any formal insolvency procedure;

11.8 All brochures, catalogues and other promotional materials are to be treated as illustrative only. Their contents form no part of any contract between us and you should not rely on them in entering into any contract with us.

11.9 Any notice by either of us which is to be served under these terms may be served by leaving it at or by delivering it to (by first class post) the other's registered office or principal place of business. All such notices must be signed.

11.10 No contract will create any right enforceable (by virtue of the Contracts (Rights of Third Parties) Act 1999) by any person not identified as the buyer or seller.

12. Entire agreement

12.1 Each of the parties agrees that save in respect of statements made fraudulently it shall have no remedy in respect of any untrue statement upon which it relied in entering this Agreement and that its only remedies shall be for breach of contract.

Appendix 8: Sales by item 2008 – 2012

Sales by Item
A&M Huese t/a Wealden Flowers

Item	2008	2009	2010	2011	2012	average
swp - Sweet Peas (bunch of 10)	£1,723.28	£2,111.20	£2,534.00	£2,030.50	£2,890.00	£2,257.80
sun - Sunflowers	£153.19	£104.83	£480.25	£958.50	£345.00	£408.35
peo - Peony (mixed colours)	£185.12	£518.44	£725.00	£362.00	£132.00	£384.51
hyd - Hydrangea	£0.00	£0.00	£0.00	£189.10	£408.00	£298.55
ant - Antirrhinum	£120.84	£241.28	£243.50	£111.50	£188.00	£181.02
sww - Sweet William	£61.88	£321.88	£106.00	£244.00	£164.00	£179.55
dah - Dahlia	£65.00	£35.88	£467.00	£273.00	£26.00	£173.38
zin - Zinnia	£61.62	£136.24	£431.00	£159.00	£72.00	£171.97
sta - Stachys (Lamb's Ear)	£0.00	£0.00	£0.00	£167.00	£147.00	£157.00
ros - Roses	£0.00	£69.99	£112.40	£198.80	£237.60	£154.70
cor - Cornflower	£258.96	£0.00	£0.00	£0.00	£45.00	£151.98
stat - Statice	£127.92	£65.52	£0.00	£0.00	£233.00	£142.15
ery - Eryngium	£0.00	£0.00	£11.50	£85.00	£306.00	£134.17
nig - Nigella	£68.64	£0.00	£0.00	£0.00	£180.00	£124.32
aga - Agastache	£0.00	£0.00	£0.00	£0.00	£117.00	£117.00
eup - Euphorbia	£0.00	£0.00	£0.00	£96.00	£111.00	£103.50
amm - Ammi (White Dill)	£0.00	£0.00	£34.50	£29.50	£219.00	£94.33
cer - Cerinthe	£0.00	£0.00	£0.00	£0.00	£90.00	£90.00
cam - Campion (Lychnis coronaria)	£0.00	£0.00	£0.00	£0.00	£86.00	£86.00
nic - Nicotiana	£0.00	£0.00	£85.00	£0.00	£0.00	£85.00
ama - Amaranthus	£0.00	£72.54	£176.50	£50.00	£40.00	£84.76
hyp - Hypericum	£0.00	£14.56	£130.00	£88.00	£88.00	£80.14
cal - Calendula (marigold)	£38.48	£0.00	£63.50	£0.00	£84.00	£61.99
cla - Clary Sage	£0.00	£0.00	£0.00	£51.00	£60.00	£55.50
phy - Physostegia	£0.00	£0.00	£0.00	£46.00	£60.00	£53.00
pop - Poppy	£63.18	£49.40	£31.50	£0.00	£88.00	£46.42
lar - Larkspur	£44.93	£0.00	£37.00	£0.00	£42.00	£41.31
ach - Achillea	£76.70	£12.48	£22.00	£10.00	£0.00	£30.30
sca - Scabiosa	£1.82	£4.68	£21.00	£4.00	£118.00	£29.90
dil - Dill	£0.00	£0.00	£20.00	£2.50	£30.00	£17.50
alc - Alchemilla Mollis	£0.00	£0.00	£18.00	£4.00	£24.00	£15.33
euc - Eucalyptus	£5.20	£0.00	£0.00	£0.00	£12.00	£8.60

Appendix 9: Gross margins

On the following pages you find the gross margins for ten different crops, based on the results at Wealden Flowers. Each gross margin is calculated for a 25 metre bed, about 1.20 m wide. We grow most crops at 3 rows per bed, with rows 0.3 metres apart. Each gross margin will specify "revenue" calculated by multiplying harvestable stems per bed by the price per stem.

The direct costs for each crop are listed under "costs": the cost for seeds according to the seed catalogues. The cost for potting soil (seedling compost) is calculated by dividing price for a bag of Klasmann organic potting soil by the number of plug trays (modules) that can be filled with one bag of compost. This works out at 92p per plug tray of 126 cells. Polypropylene ground cover (Mypex) is only included for the perennials at the cost price. Fertilisation is based on the application of organic chicken manure pellets – normally 12 scoops (3 kg) per bed.

Netting and posts refers to metal support netting which at the time of writing costs around 75p per meter. Accompanying metal posts cost around £2.50 each – these costs can be divided by 5 to reflect a lifespan of five years.

Labour costs have been calculated on a £10 per hour basis. Transplant production has been estimated at 30 minutes per tray (sowing and watering), planting at 15 minutes per tray.

Gross margin	**Amaranthus**	per 25 m bed		Hourly rate:		£ 10.00
					total:	
Revenue:	350 stems @	£ 0.40	each		£ 140.00	
					£ 140.00	
Costs:						
Seeds / plants	400 seeds/plants @	£ -	each		£ -	
Potting soil	3 modules @	£ 0.92	each		£ 2.76	
Mypex	beds @	£ 12.50	each		£ -	
Fertilisation	12 scoops @	£ 0.20	each		£ 2.40	
Netting	metres @		each		£ -	
Posts	posts @		each		£ -	
Time:						
Transplant production	90 min				£ 15.00	
Planting	45 min				£ 7.50	
Weeding and hoeing	60 min				£ 10.00	
Harvesting	90 min				£ 15.00	
					£ 52.66	
Gross Margin:					£ 87.34	

Gross margin	**Antirrhinum**		per 25 m bed			Hourly rate:	£ 10.00
			350 plants				
						total:	
Revenue:	1000	stems @	£ 0.30	each		£300.00	
						£300.00	
Costs:							
Seeds / plants	800	seeds/plants @	£ 0.01	each		£ 4.80	not every seed germinates
Potting soil	3	modules @	£ 0.92	each		£ 2.76	
Mypex		beds @	£ 12.50	each		£ -	
Fertilisation	12	scoops @	£ 0.20	each		£ 2.40	
Netting	25	metres @	£ 0.15	each		£ 3.75	cost over 5 years depreciation
Posts	16	posts @	£ 0.50	each		£ 8.00	cost over 5 years depreciation
Time:							
Transplant production	90	min	(30 min/tray)			£ 15.00	
Planting	45	min				£ 7.50	
Weeding and hoeing	60	min				£ 10.00	
Harvesting	100	min				£ 16.67	
						£ 70.88	
Gross Margin:						£229.12	

Gross margin	**Dahlia**		per 25 m bed			Hourly rate:	£ 10.00
			80 plants				
						total:	
Revenue:	240	stems @	£ 0.40	each		£ 96.00	
						£ 96.00	
Costs:							
Seeds / plants	80	seeds/plants @	£ 0.32	each		£ 25.60	(1.60 over 5 years)
Potting soil		modules @	£ 0.92	each		£ -	
Mypex		beds @	£ 12.50	each		£ -	
Fertilisation	12	scoops @	£ 0.20	each		£ 2.40	
Netting		metres @		each		£ -	
Posts		posts @		each		£ -	
Time:							
Transplant production		min	(30 min/tray)			£ -	
Planting	60	min				£ 10.00	
Weeding and hoeing	60	min				£ 10.00	
Harvesting	90	min				£ 15.00	
						£ 63.00	
Gross Margin:						£ 33.00	

Gross margin	Eryngium	per 25 m bed	Hourly rate:	£ 10.00	
			180 plants		
				total:	
Revenue:	300 stems @	£ 0.70 each		£210.00	
				£210.00	
Costs:					
Seeds / plants	200 seeds/plants @	£ 0.02 each		£ 4.00	
Potting soil	2 modules @	£ 0.92 each		£ 1.84	
Potting up	4 pot trays @	£ 1.80 each		£ 7.20	
Mypex	1 beds @	£ 2.50 each		£ 2.50	(12.50 over 5 years)
Fertilisation	12 scoops @	£ 0.20 each		£ 2.40	
Netting	25 metres @	£ 0.15 each		£ 3.75	depriciated over 5 years
Posts	16 posts @	£ 0.50 each		£ 8.00	depriciated over 5 years
Time:					
Transplant production	120 min			£ 20.00	
Planting	90 min			£ 15.00	
Weeding and hoeing	30 min			£ 5.00	
Harvesting	60 min			£ 10.00	
				£ 79.69	
Gross Margin:				£130.31	

Gross margin	Hydr Annabelle	per 25 m bed	Hourly rate:	£ 10.00	
			75 plants		
				total:	
Revenue:	300 stems @	£ 0.80 each		£240.00	
				£240.00	
Costs:					
Seeds / plants	75 seeds/plants @	£ 0.40 each		£ 30.00	(2.00 over 5 years)
Potting soil	modules @	£ 0.92 each		£ -	
Mypex	1 beds @	£ 2.50 each		£ 2.50	(12.50 over 5 years)
Fertilisation	12 scoops @	£ 0.20 each		£ 2.40	
Netting	25 metres @	£ 0.15 each		£ 3.75	depriciated over 5 years
Posts	16 posts @	£ 0.50 each		£ 8.00	depriciated over 5 years
Time:					
Transplant production	min			£ -	
Planting	min			£ -	
Weeding and hoeing	30 min			£ 5.00	
Harvesting	90 min			£ 15.00	
				£ 66.65	
Gross Margin:				£173.35	

Gross margin	**Hypericum**		per 25 m bed		Hourly rate:		£ 10.00
					75 plants		
						total:	
Revenue:	420	stems @	£ 0.25	each		£ 105.00	
						£ 105.00	
Costs:							
Seeds / plants	75	seeds/plants @	£ 0.30	each		£ 22.50	(1.50 over 5 years)
Potting soil		modules @	£ 0.92	each		£ -	
Mypex	1	beds @	£ 2.50	each		£ 2.50	(12.50 over 5 years)
Fertilisation	12	scoops @	£ 0.20	each		£ 2.40	
Netting		metres @		each		£ -	
Posts		posts @		each		£ -	
Time:							
Transplant production		min				£ -	
Planting		min				£ -	
Weeding and hoeing	60	min				£ 10.00	
Harvesting	90	min				£ 15.00	
						£ 52.40	
Gross Margin:						£ 52.60	

Gross margin	**Roses**		per 25 m bed		Hourly rate:		£ 10.00
						total:	
Revenue:	50	stems @	£ 0.70	each		£ 35.00	
						£ 35.00	
Costs:							
Seeds / plants	50	seeds/plants @	£ 0.84	each		£ 42.00	(4.20 over 5 years)
Potting soil		modules @	£ 0.92	each		£ -	
Mypex	1	beds @	£ 2.50	each		£ 2.50	(12.50 over 5 years)
Fertilisation	12	scoops @	£ 0.20	each		£ 2.40	
Netting		metres @		each		£ -	
Posts		posts @		each		£ -	
Time:							
Transplant production		min				£ -	
Planting	120	min				£ 20.00	
Weeding and hoeing	60	min				£ 10.00	
Harvesting	30	min				£ 5.00	
						£ 81.90	
Gross Margin:						-£ 46.90	

Gross margin	**Sunflowers**		per 25 m bed		Hourly rate:	£ 10.00
					total:	
Revenue:	350	stems @	£ 0.50	each	£175.00	
					£175.00	
Costs:						
Seeds / plants	400	seeds/plants @	£ 0.013	each	£ 5.20	
Potting soil	3	modules @	£ 0.92	each	£ 2.76	
Mypex		beds @	£ 12.50	each	£ -	
Fertilisation	12	scoops @	£ 0.20	each	£ 2.40	
Netting		metres @		each	£ -	
Posts		posts @		each	£ -	
Time:						
Transplant production	90	min			£ 15.00	
Planting	40	min			£ 6.67	
Weeding and hoeing	60	min			£ 10.00	
Harvesting	90	min			£ 15.00	
					£ 57.03	
Gross Margin:					£117.97	

Gross margin		**Zinnia**		per 25 m bed		Hourly rate:		£ 10.00
							total:	
Revenue:		700	stems @	£	0.30	each	£210.00	
							£210.00	
Costs:								
	Seeds / plants	400	seeds/plants @	£	0.02	each	£ 7.60	
	Potting soil	3	modules @	£	0.92	each	£ 2.76	
	Mypex		beds @	£	12.50	each	£ -	
	Fertilisation	12	scoops @	£	0.20	each	£ 2.40	
	Netting		metres @			each	£ -	
	Posts		posts @			each	£ -	
Time:								
	Transplant production	90	min	(30 min/tray)			£ 15.00	
	Planting	40	min				£ 6.67	
	Weeding and hoeing	60	min				£ 10.00	
	Harvesting	90	min				£ 15.00	
							£ 59.43	
Gross Margin:							£150.57	

The following gross margin is included as an example how a greenhouse crop is completely different from an outdoor crop in its financial performance. The cost of the greenhouse or polytunnel is not included in this calculation:

Gross margin	**Sweet Peas**		per 25 m bed		Hourly rate:	£ 10.00	
					total:		
Revenue:	3600	stems @	£	0.18	each	£648.00	
						£648.00	
Costs:							
Seeds / plants	125	seeds/plants @	£	0.05	each	£ 5.63	
Potting soil	1	modules @	£	0.92	each	£ 0.92	
Potting on	3	pot trays @	£	1.80	each	£ 5.40	
Mypex		beds @	£	12.50	each	£ -	
Fertilisation	12	scoops @	£	0.20	each	£ 2.40	
Netting	50	metres @	£	0.15	each	£ 7.50	depriciated over 5 years
Posts	8	posts @	£	0.50	each	£ 4.00	depriciated over 5 years
Max tape	1	rolls @	£	1.05	each	£ 1.05	
Silver solution	36	ml @	£	0.10	each	£ 3.60	
Time:							
Transplant production	90	min				£ 15.00	
Planting	40	min				£ 6.67	
Weeding and hoeing	60	min				£ 10.00	
Tapening	120	min				£ 20.00	
Harvesting	720	min				£120.00	
						£202.16	
Gross Margin:						£445.84	

Key word index